The Book of Missiles

BY

CLIVE E. DAVIS

DODD, MEAD & COMPANY   NEW YORK   1959

BOOKS BY CLIVE E. DAVIS
The Junior Airman's Book of Airplanes
The Book of Missiles

CONTENTS

Preface   3

Part 1 — SPUTNIK   7

Part 2 — THE MISSILE AGE   13

Part 3 — AIR-TO-AIR MISSILES   17

Part 4 — AIR-TO-SURFACE MISSILES   27

Part 5 — SURFACE-TO-AIR MISSILES   35

Part 6 — SURFACE-TO-SURFACE MISSILES   53

Part 7 — MAN IN SPACE   87

Glossary   93

Index   95

PREFACE

In the short span of fifty years since the Wright brothers' wobbly flight at Kitty Hawk, aviation has changed the complexion of the world and exerted a profound influence upon its people.

Aviation gave military men air power, the ability to lay fire upon the enemy in a manner that changed the basic concepts of warfare and revealed the air as the logical avenue for the extension of all phases of military fire power. To this objective Man has dedicated himself, turning to the almost forgotten art of rocketry as a means of propelling ballistic projectiles.

The exigency of our military requirements has given us modern air transportation well ahead of schedule and now the same urgency, through missiles, has opened the door to Space. As a result of our efforts, impelled by a fear of aggression, we are moving at hypersonic speed toward an ambiguous destiny, traveling in a confusion of complexities.

It is my hope that this little book will help many to a clearer understanding of the Missile Age by offering a perspective that could only be provided by a layman totally unhampered by any qualifications in the field.

My sincere thanks go to the many representatives of industry and their companies, to the individuals and agencies of the Army, Navy and Air Force, for the assistance given me in collecting and compiling the material presented. Let me emphasize that the text contains some purely personal opinions for which none of these kindly people should be held responsible.

My special thanks are extended to Editor John F. Loosbrock and the staff of *Air Force Magazine* for allowing me to use the excellent charts from their March 1958 edition, and to my old flying buddy, expert photographer Don Horton, for his help in selecting the photographs to be used.

CLIVE E. DAVIS

Sacramento, California

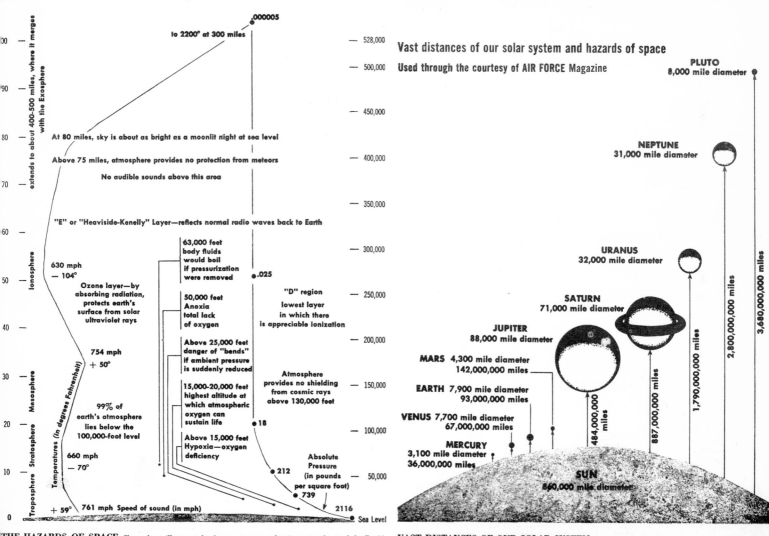

THE HAZARDS OF SPACE Chart above illustrates the dangers to man as he rises up and out of the Earth's atmosphere. From 15,000-20,000 feet is the highest altitude where atmospheric oxygen will sustain life. At 63,000 feet, blood boils. At 80,000 feet, a sealed cabin with self-contained environment is mandatory. At 130,000 feet, atmospheric shielding of cosmic rays ends. Ninety-nine percent of the atmosphere is located below the 100,000-foot level. Physiological "space equivalence" begins far below that. Above 75 miles, atmospheric shielding against meteors ends.

VAST DISTANCES OF OUR SOLAR SYSTEM and the diameters of its nine planets are illustrated here. To a Plutonian, more than 3,680,000,000 miles away, the sun would look like not much more than a star, while to a Mercurian, "only" 36,000,000 miles away, the sun would appear as a huge fiery orb in the heavens. Of all the planets, Earth seems to be ideally situated, just far enough away from the sun (93,000,000 miles) to provide balanced and comfortable temperatures, radiation, and light ranges to nurture the life that has developed on this planet over the ages.

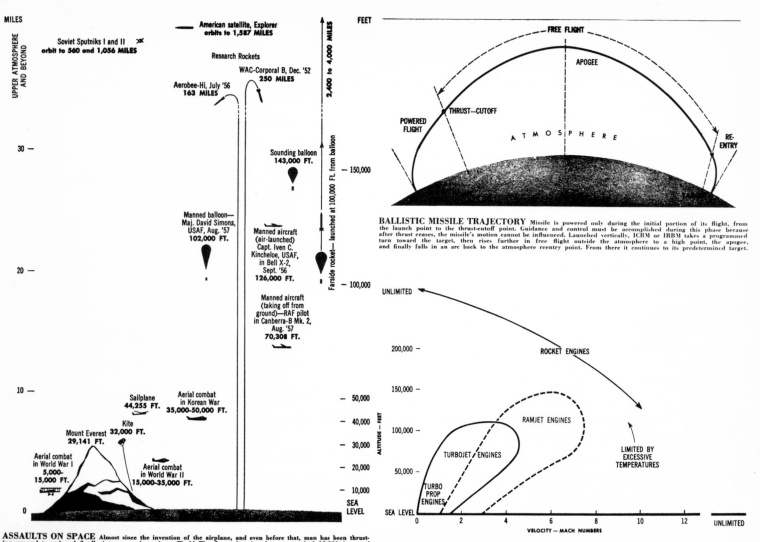

ASSAULTS ON SPACE Almost since the invention of the airplane, and even before that, man has been thrusting upward toward and finally into space. As early as World War I, combat-aircraft range reached 15,000 feet, and during World War II, combat planes attained 35,000 feet. In Korea, jets fought as high as 50,000 feet. In 1956, Capt. Iven C. Kincheloe, Jr., attained man's highest powered flight, 126,000 feet, in the Bell X-2. Maj. David G. Simons a year later, in "Man High," ascended in a balloon to 102,000 feet. Now satellites have accomplished orbits in near space.

BALLISTIC MISSILE TRAJECTORY Missile is powered only during the initial portion of its flight, from the launch point to the thrust-cutoff point. Guidance and control must be accomplished during this phase because after thrust ceases, the missile's motion cannot be influenced. Launched vertically, ICBM or IRBM takes a programmed turn toward the target, then rises further in free flight outside the atmosphere to a high point, the apogee, and finally falls in an arc back to the atmosphere reentry point. From there it continues to its predetermined target.

THE LIMITS OF AIR-BREATHING CRAFT Powered flight has taken man and his aircraft to ever-higher altitudes, and finally to the limits of the most advanced airplanes, powered by ramjets, which run out of air to "breathe" and push against at about 150,000 feet. At this point rockets take over, carrying their own "air" with them and offering the mechanical approach to spaceflight because their ability to operate in the vacuum of space is theoretically unlimited. After today's chemically powered rockets will come nuclear, ion, and even photon propulsion.

Part 1 / SPUTNIK

On October 4, 1957, the American people took a short course in Russian. They learned one word . . . *"Sputnik!"*

Within hours, thousands had looked up into the skies to catch glimpses of the first man-made satellite, a beeping contraption of complicated design, circling the Earth on schedule and telling secrets of the Universe.

Peter J. Schenk, president of the Air Force Association, called this event "the Sputnik Pearl Harbor." He saw it as an ominous warning of the technological war in which we are engaged. America awoke to the scientific ability of the Russians. For the first time, the general public became fully aware of the meaning of rockets and the missiles they propel.

Of course, rockets are not an invention of our age. The Chinese used rockets in warfare in 1232 A.D. Only a few decades later, Europeans were using them to set fire to enemy fortifications. England's Sir William Congreve developed solid-fuel rockets which carried explosives almost two miles in 1803. Some of Congreve's rockets put "the rockets' red glare" in our National Anthem. They were being fired from British ships at our Fort McHenry. American soldiers used rockets against the Mexicans in 1847.

The first American to consider rockets in connection with the conquest of space was Robert H. Goddard. He began special studies in 1909 and in 1920 wrote a paper, published by the Smithsonian Institution, describing the use of rockets to reach high altitudes. Goddard built a liquid-fuel rocket in 1926 and in 1930 fired a rocket which rose to 2,000 feet at a speed of 500 miles per hour.

World War Two brought other rockets. Infantrymen fired the bazooka at tanks and vehicles; multiple launchers aboard ships fired up to 300 rockets per minute at the enemy and aircraft used rockets against ground targets and other aircraft. However, the most important rocket to come out of World War Two was the German V-2. London and Antwerp felt the power of this missile.

The V-2 was developed by a group of German scientists and engineers, under the leadership of Dr. Walter R. Dornberger, doctor of engineering and a general officer in the German Army. Among the men in this group were Professor Hermann Oberth, who wrote in 1923 about the conquest of space, and Dr. Wernher von Braun.

7

Dr. Dornberger retired from the German Army with the rank of lieutenant general in 1947 and became a technical consultant in the guided missile program of the United States Air Force. He left the Air Force to become associated with industry in 1950. Some of his former subordinates, among them Wernher von Braun, came to the United States to aid in the development of ballistic missiles. Others of the group are now with the Russians, engaged in the same work.

After World War Two, with the help of these German scientists, we used the knowledge gained from captured German V-2 rockets to continue experiments intended to produce a long range missile which could be combined with the awesome power of the atomic and hydrogen bomb to become "the ultimate weapon" and to bring an era of "push-button warfare."

By October 4, 1957, we had come a long ways from the V-2. In fact, the day before Sputnik One startled the world, the United States Air Force fired a Farside Rocket almost 4,000 *miles* into space from Eniwetok Island. However, security requirements made it necessary to withhold this information for three weeks while the Sputnik held the news spotlight and slammed home to us the truth of Russian scientific stature.

But to go back eleven years, to 1946. At that time, the Army Air Force had already exhausted the research possibilities of the V-2 and twenty-eight new missile projects were undertaken in a complete departure from the line of scientific thinking shown by the V-2. From these projects came the engine which was to be used later in the Navaho, Redstone, Atlas, Thor and Jupiter missiles. The Army Air Force also began to investigate the possibility of launching an earth satellite. In the same year, studies were started which led to the construction of the Atlas intercontinental ballistic missile.

In 1947 we came close to making a serious blunder in our long range planning for the development of the ballistic missile. In June, fourteen months after it was started, Project MX-774 was cancelled. This was the code name for the project which produced the Atlas, the intercontinental ballistic missile which now gives us parity with the Russians.

The reason for the cancellation was the problem of re-entry. Many of the advisors to the Defense Department felt the problem of getting a nose cone back through the atmosphere was an obstacle too great to overcome. These advisors recommended consideration of a glide-type vehicle which could glide in and out of the atmosphere, gradually slowing down until the speed would be low enough to allow re-entry without intense heat from excessive speed. Later developments proved this theory also has merit and fortunately Convair, the contractor, spent company money to keep the Atlas project alive until it could be reconsidered.

But we weren't idle. We concentrated on airplane-launched, air-to-ground missiles, air-to-air missiles and ground-to-air missiles. This is the only area where we are now substantially ahead of the Soviets.

We also decided it was entirely possible to place earth satellites in orbit around the earth. This study continued on into 1948.

In September of 1948, Convair again focused attention on the Atlas Project by firing test versions of the missile and making real progress in other phases of the company-financed MX-774 project.

Throughout 1949 and 1950, we continued to develop the smaller missiles while an Air Force study group announced that long range ballistic missiles were possible. By January of 1951, another project was set up to again make a comparison of rockets and glide missiles. The one-year-old Air Research and Development Command also was ordered to study long range rockets as compared to glide vehicles. ARDC re-studied the Convair contract, which had covered the MX-774 project. In September, it was decided that Convair was using the right approach and during the next year, 1952, the Atlas program was sanctioned to get underway again. However, the decision wasn't quite official until late in the year, when a committee of the Air Force Scientific Advisory Council looked it over and approved it.

Through 1953, the missile program moved along slowly, with the most exciting development being the formation of another new committee, the Strategic Missiles Evaluation Committee, which immediately began a review of the Air Force missile program.

Nineteen hundred and fifty-four brought the conclusion that small, powerful thermonuclear weapons were possible and were ideal for missile warfare. The Air Force also re-emphasized the possibility of an earth satellite and recommended a satellite project, saying it would be valuable for reconnaissance, intelligence and getting weather information.

In 1955, two major decisions were made. Top priority was given to the Titan project, another ICBM (intercontinental ballistics missile), and the Thor IRBM (intermediate range ballistics missile) was added to the Air Force missile program.

The Air Force, Army and Navy reached basic agreements on coordinating the Thor and Jupiter IRBM programs in 1956. The Air Force turned over engines it had developed to the Army to use in the Jupiter and the Secretary of Defense directed that a part of Camp Cooke, California, be assigned to the Air Force, to become a missile-launching training center and possibly a missile-launching site.

Nineteen hundred and fifty-seven saw the initial test firings of the Atlas and Thor missiles and a re-arrangement of the ballistic missiles program. Atlas retained first priority, the Titan program was slowed down. It was recommended that the Thor and Jupiter programs be combined and all contractor over-time was stopped. A delay in the IRBM program was unavoidable.

On October 4th, 1957, Sputnik I blazed into space and focused public attention upon our total missiles program.

The initial sight was not a cheering one. But, on closer examination, it was found that, in spite of many barriers, the United States was well on the way to laying the foundation for an adequate program which could eventually lead to regaining our position in the missiles race with the Russians.

Despite stop-and-go thinking, a lack of sound leadership at times, on the higher levels, and unpredictable financial support from Congress, the persistency of the military services and industry had set the pattern for future success. There was still a drastic and compelling need for coordination and long-range planning, with a clear definition of purpose, but there was a foundation from which to begin the job ahead.

By early 1958, the American people had recovered from the Sputnik shock and had begun a sober reappraisal of what must be done to keep our way of life and the freedoms which we hold so dear and which have been so costly to acquire.

We realized we were not going to become space people overnight — nor in the next week. The process would be long and slow and very costly. And the process would have to be two-fold. As we probed into space, we must also continue to develop and improve the ballistic missile and the systems necessary for defending our nation against enemy missile attacks. We realized it might take a hundred years to give Man the ability to travel freely in space, and, as we strive for this goal, we must always remember we need at least equality in nuclear weapon systems. We saw that the announcement of the coming death of the flying Air Force, like that of Mark Twain, may have been "premature." There was every indication that missiles were but one step in the evolution from aircraft to spacecraft. In the interim, ballistic missiles would serve primarily as a supplement to manned aircraft and an extension of conventional firepower.

In March of 1958, our English cousins emphasized what may be a shortcoming of heavy missiles as a replacement for manned aircraft. The English protested violently against the building of missile launching sites in their country, arguing that such sites of stationary concrete and steel would be extremely vulnerable to enemy attack. Said the English, the Soviet Union would know the exact location of these stationary launching platforms as soon as the first shovel of dirt was turned for the construction and aimed directly at each site would be a Russian ballistic missile capable of destroying it. This protest renewed discussion of the possibility that launching sites of missiles must be completely mobile, if they are to survive enemy action. Many felt that supersonic and hypersonic manned aircraft might provide the ideal launching sites for long range missiles until such time as manned space platforms become a reality.

The United States Air Force revealed the development of a new ballistic missile with a range greater than that of any air-launched missile currently in the Air Force inventory. It would be launched initially by the B-70 chemical bomber and later by a nuclear-powered bomber.

We had problems — but we had also made progress. We were far enough along toward the conquest of space to know that we could win the technological war if we would profit by our past mistakes and continue to make a coordinated effort. We knew we had the brains, the scientists, engineers, physicists and mathematicians to do the planning and building; we had the capability of mass production to a degree that has proven unbeatable in the past, and we still had access to the resources we needed.

Our most imperative need was to acquire the organization and the capacity to develop our potentialities, together with a determination to expedite the passage through the Missile Age to the Space Age.

One of the essential requirements for winning this technological war is a thoroughly informed public. This is, indeed, an age of complexity. The temptation is great to cling to complacency, with the expedient excuse that this scientific stuff is beyond our understanding. But, actually, it can be understood if one will take the time and make the effort to learn. Lectures, books, literature and forums of various kinds are available to anyone who really wants to understand why we must work toward the conquest of Space.

Our governmental leaders are pretty generally laymen in regard to science. This period is as difficult for them as it is for the rest of us. They need the support of an informed public, capable of an intelligent understanding of current problems, to help them make sound decisions. It is our individual responsibility to learn as much as we can about the age in which we live.

We will move into the Space Age when Man moves into space. When the frontiers of knowledge advance enough to permit Man to travel in space and devise ways of using the elements of space to our benefit — perhaps to realize the military hope of using space weapon systems as a conclusive deterrent power for peace — when these advances are made, we will have entered the Space Age.

We must make sure that we do not enter this Age too late, with too little. We will have lost more than a mere technological war if this should happen.

Part 2 / THE MISSILE AGE

The Missile Age is the aero-astronautical period of time between the Air Age and the Space Age. It is a transitory period during which Man learns to fly higher and faster and longer until he can eventually move about freely and usefully in space. Already, with the exception of our large IRBM's and ICBM's, there is often a great similarity between missiles and aircraft. Only the pilot makes the difference.

The picture on page 14 is a ground view of the Regulus II, a guided missile built for the Navy by the Chance Vought Aircraft Company. This is a flight test version of the Regulus, equipped with a landing gear which permits it to be brought back, landed safely and used again.

The airplane on page 15 is the Lockheed F-104 Starfighter, a manned interceptor airplane. Standing at the front, inspecting the needle-like nose probe, is the pilot who makes this an airplane. Missiles powered by ramjet, or airbreathing, engines are actually pilotless aircraft.

Jet engines need oxygen from the air to operate. Rocket engines carry their own oxygen supply with them. This means that the operational altitude of jet engines, whether in aircraft or guided missiles, is limited to the atmosphere supplying the oxygen they require. And naturally, the rockets do not have this restriction.

Ramjet-powered missiles are usually launched by powerful rocket boosters which burn a comparatively short time but develop tremendous thrust, causing the missile to reach ramjet speed. This means that the airscoop is picking up sufficient air at a speed great enough to supply the amount of oxygen the ramjet engine must have to operate. As the ramjet engine takes over, the expended rocket boosters drop away from the missile.

Regulus II

Lockheed F-104 Starfighter

Rocket engines are of two basic types, liquid-propellant and solid-propellant. The diagram below, reproduced through the courtesy of *Air Force Magazine,* describes the two types.

We are developing at a fantastic rate, with new scientific break-throughs and discoveries on the frontier of knowledge occurring constantly. The characteristics of missiles described in this book are the minimum capabilities anticipated in design. Many improvements, such as increases in range and speed, are to be expected with further development.

In these hypersonic times, it may help us to understand new advances by knowing about the missiles which have already been designed, produced, tested and proven capable of performing the mission for which they were intended. Some of the missiles described are now obsolete, some are operational with the military services, others are still on the drawing board, while others are in production and will soon be operational. At any moment, some newly discovered scientific fact might make them all obsolete. Such is the pace of the Missile Age as Man hurtles on toward Space.

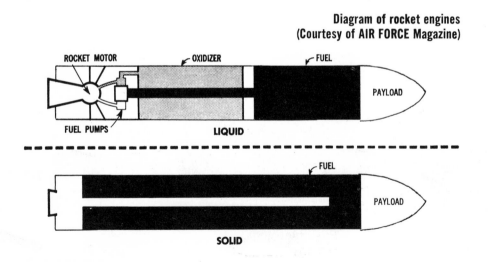

Diagram of rocket engines
(Courtesy of AIR FORCE Magazine)

ROCKET MOTOR OXIDIZER FUEL

PAYLOAD

FUEL PUMPS **LIQUID**

FUEL

PAYLOAD

SOLID

TWO TYPES OF PROPELLANTS Top cutaway shows liquid-propelled rocket's two chambers, one for fuel and the other for an oxidizer to enable the fuel to "burn" in the rocket motor, forming the powerful exhaust thrust. Storing the volatile liquids and the time required to prepare liquid rockets for launching are factors why second-generation ballistic missiles will probably all be solid-repellant (lower), whose oxidizer is contained in the fuel. In solid rocket, fuel burns uniformly out from central core. These rockets can, when operational, be fired on short notice.

Part 3 / AIR-TO-AIR MISSILES

The Air-to-Air Missile gives the airplane a significant increase in aerial fire power, allowing it an offensive and defensive capability never before possible. With certain missiles of this category, a single jet all-weather interceptor is able to successfully attack and destroy a whole flight of invading enemy aircraft and to shoot down some types of guided missiles. This interceptor fire power remains an important factor in the security of our nation. Manned aircraft are still essential to our power for peace.

While the Russians were giving top priority to their missile and space programs during the pre-Sputnik period, they were certainly not neglecting the development of manned aircraft. Their aircraft program includes nuclear-propulsion experimentation, developing bigger and better jet bombers, long-range jet fighters and jet helicopters. In early 1958, it was apparent the real reason for the announced reduction in the number of Russian medium-range Bison's was the operational status of a new jet heavy bomber comparable to the American B-52. Most alarming were the reports that they were actually out-producing us in the heavy bomber field.

All this Russian progress in the development of manned aircraft was smoke-screened by the repeated public announcements by Nikita Khrushchev that the ballistic missile has replaced the manned bomber. As Khrushchev preached that the bomber was obsolete, the Russians continued to build along the entire spectrum of manned aircraft at a rate which showed they planned to have a first-class flying air force for some time to come.

As long as this condition exists, it is comforting to know our jet all-weather interceptors carry new and terrible aerial fire power as they streak skyward on a scramble to identify an unknown aircraft. If an enemy should be "old-fashioned" enough to attack us with manned aircraft, he would find other manned aircraft, strengthened with new missile power, ready to meet him and destroy him.

This is the role of the missile in support of airpower.

THE FALCON

On the opposite page are two versions of the Hughes GAR, or "guided aircraft rocket," which is called "The Falcon." It is an air-to-air missile, produced for the use of the Air Defense Command's all-weather interceptor aircraft. The Northrop F-89H and the Convair F-102A were among the first interceptors to carry the Falcon.

On the pilot's left is the GAR-1D model Falcon. It is a radar-guided missile which can continually compute the target's position, to steer a collision course to the predicted point of impact. The accuracy of this design was proven in the developmental tests by the number of drone aircraft targets destroyed, even though the missile carried telemetering equipment, instead of tactical warheads.

The pilot has his hand on a later model of the Falcon, the GAR-2A. This model has a guidance unit which senses, at a distance of miles, the infrared radiation thrown out by invading aircraft. The infrared-guidance Falcon has tracked and blasted both F-80 jet fighters and the Matador guided missile.

Both the GAR-1D and GAR-2A are the same size. They are 6½ feet long, 6½ inches in diameter and weigh slightly more than 120 pounds. The Falcon is propelled by a rocket engine and its speed, in addition to that of the launching interceptor, far surpasses supersonic. It packs the blast of an artillery shell and one hit is sufficient to destroy any known aircraft.

The latest version of the Falcon is the GAR-9, which is designed for use with the North American Aircraft F-108, long range supersonic interceptor. The GAR-9 has a range and speed which surpasses each of its predecessors. Armed with a nuclear warhead, the GAR-9 can quickly spell obliteration of any known aircraft and it can be used as an anti-missile missile against enemy IRBM's and ICBM's.

By using both models of Falcons, the radar-guided and the infrared-guided, our fighter interceptors have a versatility which gives the pilot an ideal weapon in any kind of weather and at any altitude. Mixed loads can be used with no difficulty. The Falcon can hunt down the target regardless of any evasive action that may be attempted.

Falcon, GAR-1D and GAR-2A with F-102

THE GENIE

Shortly after 6 o'clock, on the morning of July 19, 1957, Captain Eric Hutchison lifted an F-89H Northrop "Scorpion" off the runway at Indian Springs Air Force Base, Nevada. The Scorpion carried the first atomic warhead air-to-air rocket, the Genie, produced by the Douglas Aircraft Company.

In the back seat of the F-89H was Captain Alfred "Cliff" Barbee, radar observer and weaponeer. His job was to accomplish the air-arming of the Genie and to make sure it was launched precisely at the right second.

Minutes later, at an altitude of exactly 18,000 feet, the F-89H launched the Genie. The rocket motor of the Genie began blasting a long trail of flame and the Scorpion entered a long-practiced escape pattern, to take it safely away from the point of atomic detonation.

In a matter of seconds, at the precise time planned, directly over Ground Zero, a gigantic flash of white light appeared, bathing the desert and the surrounding mountains in the intense glow. The white flash quickly contracted into an orange ball that got darker and became flat on one side and stayed there inertly in the morning sky.

Soon a misty cloud began rising from the orange ball, rising above it and encircling it. The cloud and the ball rode gently in the sky as the orange turned to reddish-purple, gradually became longer and longer, then merged with the misty cloud. The cloud rose, getting larger and larger. Finally it floated beyond the mountain, and the desert sky was clear.

In that dramatic manner did the Genie, an unguided air-to-air missile, explode the first air-to-air atomic warhead and join the operational arsenal of the Air Force.

The original model of the Genie was unguided in the sense that it had no guidance unit of its own. Its direction was determined by the path flown by the launching F-89H. A later model had a built-in guidance system which allowed it to seek, track down and destroy its target. The Genie has the ability to find and destroy a whole flight of enemy airplanes with one atomic blast. And its launching platform is a single jet interceptor.

Lieutenant General J. H. Atkinson, Commander of the Air Defense Command, congratulates Captains Eric Hutchinson and Alfred Barbee after launching of the Genie

THE SIDEWINDER AND DIAMONDBACK

The Diamondback is the latest version of the Sidewinder infrared, air-to-air missile developed at the Naval Ordnance Test Station, Chine Lake, California, and produced by General Electric and the Philco Corporation. Used by both the Navy and the Air Force, the Sidewinder is 9 feet long, almost 5 inches in diameter and weighs about 155 pounds. During developmental tests, the Sidewinder was able to shoot a flare-pot off the wing of a drone target aircraft.

Infrared is not heat waves traveling through the air. It is actually a part of the electromagnetic spectrum, just like radio and television waves, radar, light, ultra-violet light, x-rays, gamma rays and cosmic rays. Infrared travels through space with the speed of light (186,300 miles per second) and is transmitted through air, vacuum or space in the same manner as radio waves or light.

Water vapor and carbon dioxide at low altitudes can occasionally limit the effectiveness of the infrared detection and guidance system used on the Sidewinder. However, the usefulness of infrared above 30,000 feet is unlimited.

The trend for missiles and aircraft to fly higher and faster makes passive infrared detection and tracking all the more valuable. Supersonic and hypersonic aircraft and missiles are heated to high temperatures by passage through the air. This produces infrared waves and creates excellent targets for the IR (infrared) guided Sidewinder and Diamondback missiles.

The Air Force F-100 and the Navy F-9-F (shown on the opposite page) are now equipped with the Sidewinder.

The first Navy Squadrons to use the Sidewinder were Attack Squadron 46, aboard the USS *Randolph,* with the Sixth Fleet, and Fighter Squadron 211, aboard the USS *Bon Homme Richard,* with the Seventh Fleet in the Western Pacific. It is also in use by the jet all-weather interceptors of the Air Force's Air Defense Command. It offers hypersonic speed and extremely high altitude operation as a defense for our fleets at sea and for continental United States.

Navy F-9-F with sidewinder missile

THE SPARROW

The Sparrow is an air-to-air missile used by the Navy, with two versions being operational, the Sparrow I developed by the Douglas Aircraft Company and the Sperry Gyroscope Company and the Sparrow III, developed by the Raytheon Manufacturing Company. The major difference between the two is the type of guidance system used.

Sparrow I is a beam rider. It rides the radar beam of the launching airplane to the target. Immediately after launching, the flight of the missile is stabilized by a small inertial guidance system in the missile itself. Then the miniature radar receiver in the Sparrow causes the missile to follow the radar beam from the aircraft to the target. There are two disadvantages in this system. The accuracy of the missile lessens as it nears the target because the beam of the aircraft radar gets wider at that point. Also, the interceptor aircraft must hold its radar on the target until the missile strikes.

Sparrow III is radar-homing. It uses its own radar to lead it to the target. This type of radar guidance becomes more efficient as it gets closer to the target.

As can be seen in the pictures on the opposite page, (Sparrow I above; Sparrow III, below.) there is only a slight difference in the configuration (shape) of the two missiles. The nose of the Sparrow III is less pointed and the forward guide fins of the Sparrow III have a lesser degree of backward sweep than the delta platform of the Sparrow I. A newer version of the Sparrow I is under development which may replace both of the present models.

Each model is powered by an Aerojet-General solid-propellant rocket motor and each is 12½ feet long. The Sparrow I weighs about 300 pounds and the Sparrow III, with the homer radar, about 50 pounds more. Each has a speed of about Mach 2.5, or two-and-one-half times the speed of sound.

As an indication of the complexities of the missile age, it took ten years to develop the Sparrow I, due primarily to the fact that it was a pioneering effort in air-to-air missiles.

A later Navy air-to-air missile which can also be used for air-to-surface operation is the Zuni. The Zuni is 9 feet long, 3 inches in diameter, weighs about 107 pounds and has a speed of Mach 3. It is an unguided missile which will later have a built-in guidance system.

Sparrow I on aircraft

AIR LAUNCHED RESEARCH MISSILES

The exploration and eventual conquest of Space is a slow, step-by-step process. For every missile in operational use today, there are dozens of test vehicles all of which have contributed valuable knowledge leading to the success of the final missile. Among these test vehicles are four which might be considered along with the Air-to-Air Missile category because they are launched from the air.

The Rockaire, developed for the Air Force by Douglas Aircraft, is an air-launched sounding rocket, capable of carrying a 40-pound load of instruments in a search for new information about Space. The Rockaire is almost 9 feet long and 9½ inches in diameter and it has stabilizing guide fins which give it a wingspan of 1 foot, 9 inches. A DM-16 Jato engine gives the Rockaire a thrust of about 7,800 pounds and a speed several times the speed of sound.

The Cook Electric Company makes two Air Force test vehicles, the Cherokee, 25 feet long and over 4 feet in diameter, an ejection seat test vehicle, and the Skokie I and II, air-launched parachute test vehicles.

The Farside is a four-stage, solid-propellant rocket which has carried a 3½-pound package of instruments over 4,000 miles into Space. Its most successful firing came on October 3, 1957, the day before Sputnik One started to orbit.

Built by Aeronutronic for the Air Force, the Farside is launched from a balloon. The ideal situation is for the balloon to reach an altitude of 100,000 feet, at which time it is inflated to its full 200-ft. diameter. Farside is then fired up through the apex of the balloon.

Farside is 30 feet long and 8 feet in diameter. The first stage is four Thiokol Recruit Rockets which give an initial thrust of approximately 160,000 pounds. The second stage is a single Recruit rocket. The third stage has four Grand Central motors, which are also used in the ASP sounding rocket, and the final stage is a single ASP motor.

A miniature radio sends back the information acquired by the instrumentation package which is designed primarily to learn about cosmic rays, the earth's magnetic and gravitational fields, ionosphere measurements, storm effects and meteorite densities.

Part 4 / AIR-TO-SURFACE MISSILES

The Missile Age has given the military the means to revolutionize warfare. It has also imposed a complexity of new problems while offering many approaches to their solution. The most facile approach was offered by a combination of the German V-2 rocket principle and the development of the atomic bomb, making possible a long-range, land-based missile that could carry annihilation to an enemy anywhere in the world. Further refinement of nuclear bombs, permitting the same amount of destructive power to be carried in a lighter payload of explosive, gave added encouragement to this approach.

As Man has hurried toward the perfection of this type of weapon system, he has also placed increasing emphasis on a concurrent program which is based upon the concept of mobility as a fundamental requirement for successful military operations. In addition to missiles launched from fixed bases, he is also developing a family of missiles which are launched from highly mobile launching platforms.

The Navy has long been an advocate of this application of the ballistic missile and has been progressing in that direction through the development of missile-firing submarines and ships which are given long periods of mobility through the use of nuclear power for propulsion. Carrier-based aircraft provide the same launching platform mobility.

The Air Force is now developing the mobility concept beyond the initial tactical application as is proved by the announcement of the new chemically-powered B-70 manned bomber, to fill the gap between the conventional jet bomber and the nuclear-power manned bomber of the future.

Until manned spacecraft becomes a reality, the ultimate mobility of missile launching platforms can be provided by long-range, hypersonic, manned aircraft, completely maneuverable and responsive to the will of the crew.

Progress in the air-to-surface missile category assures the production of long range, air-launched missiles, in step with the requirements of the hypersonic aircraft which provide the launching platform.

THE RASCAL

The Bell Aircraft Company's Rascal has the code name GAM-63, ground attack missile. It is an air-to-surface missile or pilotless bomber, with a range of over 100 miles and a speed of about Mach 1.5. The Rascal is 32 feet long and 4 feet in diameter. The USAF Strategic Air Command's B-47 jet bombers were the first to carry the Rascal as a ground bombardment weapon. At time of design, it was thought that the Rascal's 100-mile range would allow it to be dropped from the bomber well away from enemy interceptors and defensive missiles. After attaching it to the B-47, a lower fin is assembled at the rear of the missile. The three-cylinder rocket motor which propels the Rascal burns liquid fuel. The guidance system is radar-command.

Following the steady progression characteristic of the missile age, the Hound Dog, developed by North American Aviation, is a third generation of the Rascal and it is an air-to-surface missile, designed for use by the USAF B-52 jet bomber. The 40 foot-long Hound Dog is actually a pilotless bomber, powered by a Pratt & Whitney J-52 turbojet engine. It has a delta wing and canted rudders.

The next generation after the Hound Dog is designed for air-launching from the Strategic Air Command's heavy bombers, the B-52, the supersonic B-58 and the Mach 3 chemical bomber, the B-70 (North American Aviation's WS-110A), which is powered by the General Electric J-93, using chemical fuel. Later, this missile or the next generation of it, will be air-launched by the WS-125A, nuclear powered bomber.

The successor to the Hound Dog is a single-stage, solid-propellant ballistic missile. Use of a solid propellant allows an important reduction in weight as compared to the original IRBM's (intermediate range ballistic missiles) and, with its launching mobility at better than Mach 3 speeds, offers a hard-to-detect retaliatory force which will prolong the effective usefulness of the conventional manned bomber far into the astronautics age.

Continued development along this line is intended to give the air-to-surface missile an ICBM (intercontinental ballistic missile) range and capability while we also progress toward manned military spacecraft.

Bell Rascal guided missile being launched from a Boeing B-50

THE BULLPUP

Navy FJ-4 Fury fighter aircraft carry the Bullpup, a visually tracked command guided air-to-ground missile which is used with great accuracy against such pinpoint targets as small craft, trucks and tanks. One pilot hit a 4-inch square target on his first run with the Bullpup.

This Martin-built missile is 11 ft. long, one foot in diameter and weighs about 600 pounds. It is propelled by a solid-propellant rocket engine, located in the aft section. The warhead is in the center section and the forward section and nose cone carry the radio guidance system. The Bullpup travels at Mach 2 speeds.

The pilot's control reference is his gunsight. Visual guidance is naturally limited to line-of-sight and cannot be used in inclement weather. Control signals are obtained with the pilot operating the control stick with his left hand. These signals are translated into radio commands which are transmitted to the missile's radio receiver.

Stabilizing fins mounted on the engine section of the Bullpup are arranged to impart spin to the left for stabilization. Control surfaces are kept operating in the proper plane by the action of a vertical reference gyro in the guidance section.

The Bullpup carries a conventional warhead which is contact fuzed. It could also use a proximity fuze, if there should be a need for this type of missile.

The Bulldog, the next generation of the Bullpup, has a greater range and could carry a nuclear warhead if the situation demanded.

The Bullpup is the result of the Korean War. Navy fighters needed an answer to effective enemy anti-aircraft fire and a way to avoid having to fly into canyons to get at enemy positions. They wanted a missile which could be released beyond the range of ground fire, yet could still be controlled to the target. While it was developed too late to help the situation which inspired it, the Bullpup now gives the Navy a good ground-support capability. In the event of a limited, or "brush-fire" war, the Bullpup would be an excellent tactical weapon against enemy ground forces.

Six Bullpup missiles are carried by the FJ-4 Fury.

An advanced version of the Bullpup, called the White Lance, is used by the Air Force on the F-100 and F-105 jet fighters.

WAGTAIL

Another Air Force air-to-surface guided missile is the Wagtail, developed by Minneapolis Honeywell for use by fighter-type aircraft. The Wagtail has a relatively simple inertial guidance system which controls it to the target after release by the airplane.

Inertial guidance systems have increased steadily in accuracy with further development and can be combined with such novel devices as the voice command guidance system. This system depends upon the fact that certain vowel and vowel-like sounds are almost identical for all male voices. The technique makes the missile respond to actual voice commands given by an operator watching the flight of the missile on a radar scope.

CORVUS

A Navy missile in the same air-to-surface category as the Wagtail is the Corvus, built by Temco and used as a tactical weapon by fighter aircraft. The Corvus has still another novel guidance system. It is initially controlled by the launching airplane, but in the final stage of its flight to the target, it homes on enemy radar stations. Thus the very device used by the enemy to detect incoming missiles serves as an attraction for the Corvus.

CROSSBOW

An air-to-surface missile developed by Northrop Aircraft is called the Crossbow and uses the same system of homing in on enemy radar as the Corvus. The Crossbow is quite similar to the Wagtail and Corvus in range and performance and it is in the tactical weapon class.

GIMLET

The Navy's latest air-to-surface missile is called the Gimlet and is designed for use by carrier-based aircraft for fleet activities or for general surface tactical use much the same as the other weapon systems in the air-to-surface class.

Succeeding generations of this missile type will have greater range and more devastating fire power and probably new guidance systems, or combinations of the control devices now being employed.

GREEN QUAIL

The Green Quail is one of the first of a whole new family of electronic countermeasures, or diversionary missiles, whose purpose is to confuse the enemy and decoy their attacking interceptors and missiles away from our bombers.

Because of the mission assigned this type missile, little can be told about it at this time.

FUTURE AIR-TO-SURFACE MISSILES

As the need for mobile launching platforms for long range ballistic missiles becomes more and more apparent, the air-to-surface category of missiles will undergo extensive changes. The trend will be for larger missiles with greatly extended range and the capability of carrying nuclear and megaton warheads. Indicative of this trend is the proposal made by Convair Division of General Dynamics Corporation in early 1958.

A ramjet powered weapon system, capable of Mach 6 speed, could be carried to the point of launching by the B-58 supersonic bomber. The missile, or pilotless bomber, would have a range of approximately 3,000 miles. The B-58 could transport it about 1,000 miles toward the target, release it and still be able to fly as much as 4,000 miles back to the home base. The ramjet weapon system would weigh 12,000 pounds, travel above 100,000 feet and deliver a payload of about 1,000 pounds.

Another application of the ramjet principle which could open up limitless possibilities in the larger air-to-surface missile field is the mono-atomic or recombination ramjet. It gets its propulsive energy from the heat-producing recombination of free oxygen atoms in a narrow altitude area about 60 miles above the earth. The chemical feasibility of using the oxygen atoms available in the upper atmosphere to propel a missile was first proven by the Air Force Office of Scientific Research. Aerojet-General Corporation conducted similar studies of this possible propulsion source.

Theoretically, the mono-atomic ramjet could operate forever on an inexhaustible supply of free energy. In actual practice, the length of time the engine would continue to run would be determined by the material used in its construction. It is estimated the wear-out time of the engine would be a matter of months.

It is within the realm of possibility that a missile propelled by an engine of this type could be kept airborne for months, under complete control, ready to be directed at any target on earth.

Studies have been made for some time at the University of California Radiation Laboratory, at Livermore, California, which may lead to nuclear propulsion engines for rockets. The theory being developed is that of using a nuclear reactor to heat the inrushing air of a ramjet engine, making it possible to sustain heat longer and keep the missile airborne for a correspondingly longer period of time. Such a missile could conceivably be launched by the WS-125A nuclear-powered bomber which would already have the safeguarding shielding which might be required for crew protection from the effects of radiation.

One disadvantage of the recombination ramjet would be its relatively slow speed. Depending upon the exact available amounts of free oxygen in the upper atmosphere, the size of the engine required may cause the overall configuration of the rocket to be such that speeds of Mach 2 or less will be the maximum obtainable. However, even these speeds would be acceptable when the altitude of operation is considered.

The mission of future ramjet missiles will not be entirely offensive. They may be used by Strategic Air Command bombers as defensive weapons which can be released to destroy attacking enemy interceptors, thereby allowing the bomber to continue on to place the conventional atomic or hydrogen bomb on the intended target. Actually, this is one of the uses of the Hound Dog missile which places it in the diversionary, or countermeasures category.

As the program continues to develop, more and more emphasis will be placed upon expanding the strategic uses of the air-to-surface missile.

Part 5 / SURFACE-TO-AIR MISSILES

The surface-to-air missile is a weapon for use against invading enemy aircraft and, in its more advanced form, against incoming enemy missiles.

The first of the missiles in this category were developed at the request of the Army and Navy, for these armed services saw the ground-to-air missile as a natural extension of antiaircraft artillery. Each service went on to propose improvements upon the original design which would produce a weapon system capable of the utmost defense against enemy missiles.

In the initial phases of development, the surface-to-air missile and the apparatus to launch it constituted a complete isolated weapon system. As a greater degree of sophistication was attained, the missile itself became simply an essential, integrated part of the entire defense system. Equipment to detect, identify and track an enemy missile, then control the defending missile on a path to intercept the target, was simply added to the missile and its launching device, to compose a complete weapon system.

To make this missile truly effective, various types of radar were designed especially for the weapon system employing it. Computers were developed to establish track, determine range and other pertinent data with a speed and accuracy of which the human mind is not capable. All three military services have now developed weapon systems of this type.

The Air Force has produced several missiles of this category. They range from one type which can be picked up by remote electronic control by a jet aircraft and guided on to the target to a complete antimissile missile weapon system which could be used as the basic national defense against enemy IRBM's and ICBM's. Both the Army and Navy have similar proposals for missile defense systems.

The surface-to-air missile will continue into the foreseeable future as an essential element of our national defense. It will be combined with advanced means of detection and guidance, to act as an increasingly effective protection against invading missiles and aircraft.

NIKE-HAWK SYSTEM

The Nike was the first surface-to-air missile to be deployed around the United States as antiaircraft protection for key Air Force bases. Developed by engineers of the Army Ordnance Corps and built by the Douglas Aircraft Company, the Nike has progressed through several model phases, from the original Nike, Nike-Ajax, Nike-Hercules to the latest version, the Nike-Zeus. Range of the missiles has progressed from 25 miles to about 100 miles.

The Nikes have been propelled by a solid propellant rocket engine, constructed by Western Electric. The Nike-Hercules is equipped with a rocket booster and has a nuclear capability. The Hercules is 27 feet long and 2½ feet in diameter.

To supplement the Nike System, the Hawk guided missile, developed and produced by the Raytheon Manufacturing Company, was added to cover low-level approaches by enemy aircraft. The Hawk is 16 feet long, 14 inches in diameter and has an Aerojet solid-propellant rocket engine. The Hawk's radar detection system is specially designed to detect low-flying aircraft in the areas not covered by conventional radar. The Hawk can be used as a fixed base weapon or it can be easily moved, requiring only a mobile launching device. The Marine Corps adopted it as a mobile field weapon. It has a range of approximately 22 miles.

The Nike-Ajax is 20 feet long and one foot in diameter. With a solid-propellant booster added, it weighs about one ton. The booster places the Ajax in the two-stage category. It is shaped like a dart, with delta-shaped cruciform fins near the nose and also near the after end. The booster, too, has stabilizing fins near the base. After a period of initial thrust, during which the Ajax attains supersonic speed, the booster section drops off and the rocket motor of the missile takes over. The warhead, carried in the body of the basic missile, is designed to explode only when in flight.

Left: Nike-Hercules
Right: Nike-Hawk

THE TALOS-TARTAR

The Talos is a Navy surface-to-air missile designed for use with the fleet. A land version is being used by the Army. The McDonnell Aircraft Corporation Talos is 20 ft. long, 2½ ft. in diameter and has a speed of over Mach 2. The initial range was about 25 miles but this has been improved to nearer a 100-mile range.

The *Galveston* was the first Talos cruiser to join the fleet. The Navy has since indicated that the entire Talos weapon system was handicapped by the air-search radar installed on the ship. The maximum range of the *Galveston's* radar was about 200 miles. One of the difficulties in obtaining greater radar range lies in the heavy weight of the rotating antenna required.

The Talos can use either conventional or nuclear warheads and acts as antiaircraft protection for the fleet. It has a limited anti-missile capability. The latest version of the Talos has a speed near Mach 10 but its shipboard use is minimized by radar range limitations.

The Convair Tartar is the newest and smallest of the Navy's guided missiles in the surface-to-air category. It is designed for use from ships as small as destroyers and for secondary batteries aboard cruisers.

The Tartar has one solid-propellant rocket engine and a range of approximately 10 miles. It is built by Convair under an engineering and production contract with the Navy Bureau of Ordnance.

Thirteen guided missile destroyers will eventually use the Tartar and three heavy cruisers, the *Chicago,* the *Albany* and the *Fall River,* which are being converted into missile cruisers, will also use the Tartar.

Both the Talos and the Tartar are examples of how missiles complement and, in some cases, replace the conventional means of fire power formerly used. The Tartar, for instance, replaces five-inch guns, giving more fire power in less space and weight.

The Talos is propelled by a ramjet engine and is part of an automatic weapon system which picks up a target about 100 miles away, computes the range, makes corrections as needed, loads and fires itself, with men required only for monitoring the action. Guidance is beam-riding and passive homing.

The Talos program is an example of inter-service cooperation.

Talos in flight

THE TERRIER

Built by the Convair Division of the General Dynamics Corporation, the Terrier is a supersonic antiaircraft missile designed to guard the Navy's fleet against enemy air attack in any weather. The Terrier is 15 feet long, has a wing span of 4 feet and weighs 1,100 pounds. It has a ceiling of over 50,000 feet. Using a powerful rocket booster for launching, the Terrier is powered by one solid-propellant rocket engine and has a top speed of Mach 2.5. It is used in twin pairs aboard ships and has a range of about 20 miles. The Terrier is beamriding, following the radar beam of the launching ship to the incoming enemy target.

One version of the Terrier is used by the Marine Corps as a ground-launched antiaircraft missile. It uses a mobile launcher and has a range of about 10 miles.

In its role as supersonic protector of the fleet, the Terrier was first installed aboard the cruisers, USS *Boston* and USS *Canberra,* and the destroyer, USS *Gyatt.* Many other destroyer-type ships now carry the Terrier batteries.

The Terrier is the daddy of the Talos and the offspring of the Bumblebee. The Japanese kamikaze bombers of World War Two were the inspiration for this family of missiles. It soon became obvious that the conventional antiaircraft weapons of the time could not cope with such suicidal attacks, so experiments were started which finally led to the production of the Talos.

The Applied Physics Laboratory of Johns Hopkins University began a project in late 1944, with the immediate goal of developing ramjet supersonic missiles and the guidance systems they would need. By 1945, a test vehicle with only a six-inch diameter was fired as the first experimental verification of the ramjet principle of supersonic missiles. By then, the project was known as "Bumblebee."

A series of test vehicles was consequently developed, pushing the speed beyond Mach 2 and building bigger missiles. One of these test vehicles, used to develop stability and control parameters, was removed from the test category and refined into an interim missile named the Terrier. The Terrier, in turn, was used as the basis for the original objective of the developmental project, the bigger, longer-range but slightly slower, Talos.

Meantime, the Terrier continues to be an important weapon of the Navy.

Terrier aboard ship

MISSILE DEFENSE SYSTEMS

Any defense system against enemy missiles will probably use surface-to-air missiles as a basic element so this may be an appropriate place to discuss plans for these defense systems.

The next generation of detection system after the DEW (Distance Early Warning) Line will probably be called the Ballistic Missile Early Warning System and it will be incorporated with an anti-missile missile system, designed to accomplish the destruction of enemy missiles before they can reach their target. This phase of the Missile is of primary importance and into its solution are going the knowledge and talents of our most experienced scientists, engineers and military experts with science — the military and industry working hand-in-hand. It is important that the general public keep well informed on this essential need and so be in a position to influence sober and effective judgment in the selection and use of the system which will best provide the protection we must have.

The basis of the Ballistic Missile Early Warning System will be two long-range radar stations located at Fairbanks, Alaska, and at Thule, Greenland. These long-range detection stations will be capable of covering the entire Russian land mass and will utilize two types of radar equipment, each type able to detect incoming missiles at ranges up to 3,000 miles. Because of different beam widths, each of the radars will have a particular function.

The first type will be a *Surveillance Radar,* designed to detect any Russian-launched missile at the earliest possible moment. In order to do this, at each site surveillance radar will continuously sweep an assigned segment of the Russian airspace. The two stations together will thus provide constant and overlapping coverage of the entire Soviet land mass and ostensibly will immediately detect any launching.

These surveillance radars are improved versions of the AN/FPS-17, which has long been used from bases in Turkey to track Russian missile test firings. The earlier type radar had a range of about 1,000 miles but the refined version has the required 3,000-plus-mile range.

The Soviet pressure brought upon Turkey for a period in 1957 was probably due to the Russian knowledge that the United States was using Turkish bases to track the flights of intermediate and long-range Soviet missiles. Beginning in 1955, long before the advent of Sputnik One, the American radar stations, using the AN/FPS-17 radar to monitor Russian missiles, were supplying our government with information about the Russian ability to fire and control both intermediate and long-range missiles.

The major Russian ballistic missile test center was then at Krasnyy Yar, between Stalingrad and Saratov. The intermediate missile test range ran southwest from this center, with the impact area 1,000 miles away in the Uzbek Desert, close to the Afghanistan border. The long-range missiles were being fired just a little north of due east to an impact area in the sea beyond Vladivostok, a distance of slightly over 4,000 miles. Our radar was able to track the entire path of the intermediate range missiles and to determine the trajectory of the long-range missiles.

Other AN/FPS-17's were used from a base at Laredo, Texas, to track U.S. missiles fired from White Sands Proving Grounds, in New Mexico.

The mission of the improved versions of this long-range surveillance radar in the Ballistic Missile Early Warning System will be to detect and provide rough trajectory data on incoming missiles. A new type of antenna will permit the use of split-beams, vertically offset by a few degrees, to sweep back and forth horizontally at a very rapid rate. From the azimuth angle of intersection by a missile, the angular displacement between these offset beams, plus time of travel, will allow a computer to make rough determination of the missile's trajectory. This information goes to the second type of radar.

The second type of radar at each of the two sites is similar to the Lincoln Laboratory's Millstone Hill Radar, first installed at this location near Westford, about 30 miles north of Boston, Massachusetts.

The purpose of this narrow-beam radar is two-fold. First, it tracks the missile long enough to make a positive identification that the blip is really a missile on a ballistic trajectory and not a meteorite. It then obtains data for computing point-of-launch and point-of-impact. A special transistorized computer will use the data to process this information. Because of the narrow-beam characteristics, this second radar is entirely dependent upon the surveillance radar to pick up the target. Without the rough trajectory information and the direction of approach, the narrow-beam would stand little chance of picking up the missile in time.

It might be well to mention that this system is mostly theoretical. Concern has been voiced over the ability of the system to give the required fifteen minutes' warning time. Doubt has been expressed that anyone in government would be ready to rely upon information from the system without additional confirmation. The consequences of launching an unjustified counter-missile attack can well be realized.

The Millstone installation at Westford is for the specific purpose of studying problems of missile defense. Another radar of this type is used at Prince Albert, Canada, operating under Canadian control, for the study of meteorites and the aurora borealis. Eventually, this site will be integrated into the Ballistic Missile Early Warning System, as a backup against saturation attacks and to give a degree of confirmation of the initial radars at the basic sites.

Industry is offering several other systems, one being a long-range radar installed at target site, capable of covering a 30-degree ICBM approach corridor. However, this would provide no defense against submarine-launched missiles.

This basic part of the Ballistic Missile Early Warning System, described to this point, covers only the surveillance, detection and identification phases. How the active defense phase is to be accomplished is still a matter of debate. The Army proposes a "point defense" system, the Air Force insists we need "area defense." The basic differences focus on the distances from intended target at which an incoming missile would be destroyed.

The Army system of point defense is called the Nike-Zeus System, named for the missile which supplies the fire power. This system would use three types of radar.

Upon warning of pending attack from the Ballistic Missile Early Warning System, *Nike-Zeus surveillance* radar would continuously scan the expected direction of attack out to about 1,000 miles. This is based upon the conclusion that an incoming missile, once it had established a trajectory as reported by the Ballistic Missile Early Warning System radar, would not change its course or trajectory to the intended target. As the surveillance radar picks up the missile, it assigns it to the second radar in the system, the acquisition radar.

The acquisition radar has a range of about 600 miles. It locks onto the incoming missile and tracks it long enough to determine an accurate trajectory, then passes the target and the trajectory data on to the third type of radar, the tracking radar.

The tracking radar, with a range of about 200 miles, is actually a system using dual radar sets. One set, upon getting the assignment of a target from acquisition radar, will track the incoming missile. The second set of the dual system will track the Nike-Zeus missile fired to intercept the enemy missile. Both sets continuously supply information to a computer, the one with data on the incoming missile, the other with data on the intercepting friendly missile. This computer has a *limited ability* to guide the Nike-Zeus to a point of interception with the incoming missile.

You will note the final radar element in this system has a range of only about 200 miles. This means that, with all this complex radar complement, the point defense system using Nike-Zeus can only hope to make an intercept and kill about 75 miles from the intended target.

To oversimplify the Wizard system, proposed by the Air Force, it would use an effective multi-purpose radar, having a 1,000-mile range, with a very high degree of discrimination between warheads and decoys and the capability of intercepting all airborne vehicles with a long range, solid fuel missile.

The Army also has another missile defense system called the Plato System. This is actually another application of the Nike-Zeus system and is designed to protect field armies and critical installations overseas. This system might also be extended to NATO countries and to American cities and installations, for protection against submarine-launched IRBM's. The main distinguishing feature is that the Plato system is highly mobile, using a number of special vans, while the Nike-Zeus is a fixed base system.

To understand the immensity of the missile defense problem, it may be well to examine some of the possible means of defense, other than by anti-missile missiles, and to note some of the weak spots which will hamper any defensive action.

Here are possible ways of countering incoming missiles.

High kinetic velocity of an incoming ICBM might be used for defensive purposes by exploding a cloud of sand-like particles in its path. Impact erosion might be serious enough to alter the re-entry characteristics of the nose cone and cause the missile to explode itself.

In the upper atmosphere, where the intense nuclear radiation from an atomic blast is not attenuated by air, fissionable material in the enemy warhead might be exploded, or transmuted into non-fissionable material, by a countering atomic blast.

Because the requirements for nose cone re-entry are very stringent, it might be possible to destroy a warhead by raising its temperature with a nuclear blast prior to its re-entry. In any plan to use nuclear materials in anti-missile missiles, it is important to note that the United States is not now producing enough fissionable material to meet such a requirement in addition to our other commitments.

On the other side of the ledger, emphasizing the acute complexity of missile defense, is a consideration of decoys and the problems they pose.

Both the United States and Russia are developing decoys. The Martin Company is making a flock of decoys to protect the Titan ICBM. A new generation of problems will face any missile defense system by the time the system becomes operational!

The Soviet is known to have a technique which separates the actual warhead from the missile, then explodes the missile casing, engine and fuel tanks to create clouds of decoys both ahead of and behind the incoming warhead. Radar must be built which is sufficiently discriminating to identify the warhead from decoys, if either the Nike-Zeus or the Wizard system is to be successful.

One possible way in which radar could overcome the decoy threat is by the questionable detection at re-entry method.

At re-entry into the heavier atmosphere, decoys will slow a great deal more than the warhead because of their lower mass. Identity, of course, will then be simple. However, at that time, the missile would be only four seconds from target impact, which does not allow much time to launch an anti-missile missile and expect it to make a kill.

Another possibility lies in improved radar equipment. If radar can be made sufficiently accurate and have the range to track the enemy missile from almost immediately after it is launched, through to the time of fragmentation, after fragmentation the particle following the original trajectory could be presumed to be the warhead. However, this is a system based upon presumption and therefore may not prove too reliable.

Perhaps the best solution lies in some of the many proposals being made by industry for radar equipment which will be able to accomplish accurate detection through target analysis. In this case, "target" refers to the incoming enemy missile. Some companies propose what they call "fine structure analysis of radar echoes." This would give information on the incoming missile in regard to its velocity, scintillation, deceleration and other characteristics which could be used to discriminate between actual missiles and decoys. Many scientists feel such radar is entirely possible but the big problem lies in producing it.

The key to the whole problem of missile defense seems to be the requirement for a better type of radar. The Air Force will sponsor and supply appropriations for this important radar development.

A more advanced anti-missile concept again points to the apparent inevitability of manned aircraft continuing to play a dominant role in air power. It is suggested that fixed base launching sites of either the Nike-Zeus or Wizard type be supplemented by long-range, nuclear-powered, manned interceptors, with a Mach 3 plus capability, to be placed on patrol and to be available to be thrown into action at a moment's notice on the basis of information from the advanced sites of the Ballistic Missile Early Warning System. Thus, the intercept range would be increased, keeping the point of interception farther away from the intended impact area.

Such a mission might well be undertaken by the nuclear-powered bomber, the WS-125A, now under development. Combining as it does an almost limitless time aloft (crew fatigue being the only reason for landing) with the potentialities of air-launched, ramjet ballistic missiles, the possibilities of this extended defense system seem to be entirely feasible. It can be compared to the use in the past of the Lockheed RC-121, airborne early warning and control aircraft, in extending our radar warning network farther out from our home shores.

No matter what eventual system of defense is used, the problem of intercepting incoming enemy missiles will always remain a critical one. One thing is certain. A much more sophisticated radar, or other means of detection, must be developed and must be employed in sufficient depth and quantity to anticipate any saturation attack.

Extensive experimentation now underway in the field of electromagnetic energy may provide a system of detection which could augment the present radar techniques that are being improved all the time that they are being used.

Such a detection technique would be based upon the fact that part of the energy released by a nuclear explosion is radiated as electromagnetic energy. This causes a radio signal near the bottom of the very low frequency band which is guided by the surface of the earth and the ionosphere to channel it over long distances with little attenuation. To locate exactly the point of such a nuclear blast would require merely a comparison of the arrival times of the signal at three different receiving stations.

In the firing of a missile, the column of ionized gas trailing behind the missile also acts as a low-frequency antenna and sufficient energy goes into a similar very low frequency signal to make it detectable thousands of miles away.

The Navy has been carrying on experiments for some time into the possibility of using known deep water ocean sound ducts which conduct sound with little attenuation, as a means of submarine detection. Another system involves multiple refraction of sound waves as they penetrate the denser layers of water. These waves curve back to the surface at distances of approximately 35 miles and are then reflected by the surface. The big problem is the separation of the submarine noise from the noises made by other vessels and the natural noises of the ocean.

There is also experimentation into the possibility of propagating very low frequency radio waves through the strata of the earth's crust, with the rock strata acting as a wave-guide. This would probably be the only application of the electromagnetic principle which would provide detection of an underground nuclear explosion.

The Russians are equally as advanced in these studies as we are and appear to be devoting considerable time and research in this area. There is no reason to believe we have a monopoly in the field.

Whatever course the development of detection devices may take, we cannot escape the fact that an effective method of detecting and intercepting enemy missiles must be found. The only alternative must be to reconcile ourselves to the acceptance of painful losses in case of enemy attack and to continue to depend indefinitely upon a massive retaliatory power as an assurance of survival.

It could well be that this method of accurate detection will come from a totally unexpected source. This has happened so often in the past. Perhaps work in the field of magnetohydrodynamics, the study of the interaction between magnetic fields and electrically conducting fluids and gases, will lead science into new avenues of solution to this perplexing problem of detection.

The knowledge we already have of surface-to-air missiles indicates we are capable of producing the anti-missile missile. The main problem which must still be solved is that of infallible detection, identification and guidance of the anti-missile missile to its target.

This objective could be a futile hope. If a system of missile defense with 100 per cent reliability is produced, it will be the first time in the history of Man and his wars that any defense system has been totally effective. The old adage that "a good offense is the best defense" has yet to be disproved. Maybe the Missile Age can bring this about.

THE BOMARC

For a period of time, the Bomarc was probably the nearest thing to the ultimate weapon the Missile Age has been able to produce. This Boeing interceptor missile, designed for defense against enemy bombers, has a speed of Mach 4 and a range of at least 400 miles. Faster than any present fighter aircraft and able to operate at over 100,000 feet altitude, the Bomarc is more than a match for any bomber ever produced.

In early tests, the Bomarc was launched automatically from a control point almost 20 miles from the actual launching site, was controlled to a correct course to intercept a target drone, was then directed by its own guidance system to destroy the drone over 100 miles away. Initial control is by ground command, then the Bomarc's radar homing system takes over to track down the enemy bomber.

An Aerojet-General liquid fuel launching rocket is used to start the Bomarc on its flight. The missile flies inverted, on its back, until ramjet speed is reached. When ramjet starting velocity is attained, the launching rocket cuts out and two Marquardt 28-inch ramjet engines propel the Bomarc on to the target at 4 times the speed of sound.

Being capable of carrying a nuclear warhead, the Bomarc has a far greater capability than non-air-breathing, ground-to-air missiles. It is launched straight up in a matter of minutes after a warning is received. Seconds after the button is pushed, the Bomarc has disappeared on its way to intercept the enemy bomber. It is able to maneuver in the air, just like a piloted interceptor, but at a greater speed and higher altitude.

This pilotless interceptor is 47 feet long, has a wing span of 18 feet and the fuselage is about 3 feet in diameter. It weighs about 15,000 pounds at launching.

About 74 acres of ground are used to form a Bomarc launching site. The missile destroys itself upon impact with the target.

With that range of 400 miles or more, and a speed of Mach 4, the Bomarc can knock down a bomber at a distance that greatly exceeds the capability of any true ground-to-air missile now in use.

The Bomarc leaves us little to fear from enemy bombers.

Bomarc Interceptor missile being fired from a technical launcher shelter

THE BULL GOOSE

One of the latest ground-launched missiles has the unusual name of the Bull Goose. The Goose is a delta-wing air-breather and is a diversionary missile which is launched with missiles or manned bombers to act as a decoy to attract enemy defense system devices away from the real missiles or bombers.

The Bull Goose is built by the Fairchild Engine and Airplane Corporation for use by the Air Force's Strategic Air Command. It is powered by a Fairchild J-83 turbojet engine which produces about 2,000 pounds' thrust.

The Ramo-Woolridge Corporation provides the electronic countermeasures equipment carried in the Bull Goose.

Other Surface-to-Air Missiles

The imperative need for defense against enemy missiles continues to keep an intensified emphasis upon the design and development of more efficient ground-launched missiles.

While the present state of the art finds the missile itself superior to the systems of detection and tracking which must work with it, no time is being lost in making improvements in the missiles that carry the final destructive blow.

Even though the initial interception of incoming missiles may eventually be assigned to manned weapon systems, controlling air-launched anti-missile missiles, the total concept of defense in depth will always require ground-launch missiles as the last-ditch element of defense against an enemy strike. For this reason, we can expect to see many new missiles developed in this category.

Part 6 / SURFACE-TO-SURFACE MISSILES

The Surface-to-Surface Missile is a logical extension of artillery, augmenting or replacing the methods formerly used to bring destruction to an enemy. It affects ground artillery, naval guns and aerial fire power. It has a more profound effect in the case of the latter because aerial fire power is produced by a weapon system which includes manned aircraft and is not merely composed of a type of weapon. This system comprises the aircraft, which is the launching platform, the crew which operates the aircraft and the actual weapon itself.

It is presently anticipated that the Air Force will use both manned and unmanned systems into the foreseeable future, with the percentage of unmanned vehicles gradually becoming greater than that of manned aircraft. Evolution from aircraft to spacecraft can alter these estimates in either direction.

An examination of the inventory of surface-to-surface missiles tends to refute the oft-heard charge of missile-duplication because of inter-service rivalry. There is no denying the fact of inter-service competition, nor can we overlook the constant exchange of technical information among the services. The important fact is that the present inventory of missiles does not show any of the alleged duplications.

For the most part, each service has developed the missiles it needs for an intelligent extension of the weapon systems demanded to perform its normal missions. The Jupiter, though developed by the Army, is assigned to the Air Force. The Polaris, because of the type of launching platform available only to the Navy, is a natural Navy weapon, supporting other service missiles of similar range.

The bulk of our staggering missile expenditures goes into the production of IRBM's and ICBM's, intended to augment or replace strategic air power. Fortunately, from this development also comes a considerable amount of the information we require to penetrate Space. For this reason alone, they may be worth their cost.

As the haunting suspicion arises of the vulnerability of any stationary platform, even if it is underground, we still have no alternative but to continue the development of IRBM's and ICBM's. As long as both we and the Russians have them, we are, together, inextricably caught in the web of the Peenemunde tradition.

U. S. ARMY MISSILES

THE LACROSSE

The Lacrosse close tactical support, surface-to-surface missile was requested by the Marines, developed by the Cornell Aeronautical Laboratory, produced by the Glenn L. Martin Company and eventually become an Army project, with the Marines sharing the weapon system.

The Marines wanted a weapon that would destroy hard-top targets such as bunkers and pillboxes and thought this weapon might be delivered to the target by a helicopter. The Cornell Aeronautical Laboratory did extensive research and analysis of the hard-top target problem and concluded that a truck-mounted missile system would be more effective, reliable and economical. This decision was accepted by both the Marines and the Army.

The command-guided Lacrosse is 20 feet long and is powered by a solid-propellant rocket which gives it a range of 8 to 10 miles.

THE DART

The Dart is an anti-tank missile, controlled by optical guidance. The winged missile is 5 feet long, has a wing span of 3 feet and is about 8½ inches in diameter. The Dart is propelled by a smokeless solid-propellant rocket.

THE HONEST JOHN-LITTLE JOHN

The Honest John surface-to-surface missile was developed by Army Ordnance and manufactured by Douglas Aircraft. It is 27 feet long, has fins spanning 8 feet and is 2½ feet in diameter. It was initially deployed in Europe and Japan, has a nuclear capability and a range of about 15 miles. A single solid-propellant rocket engine is its power source. It is unguided.

Companion to the Honest John is the Little John, 12 feet long and also unguided. One foot in diameter, the Little John also has a solid-propellant rocket and is employed as a supplement to the Honest John, not a replacement for it. It is also manufactured by Douglas.

Little John makes up for some of the tactical capability which Honest John did not possess.

Douglas Honest John being launched

THE CORPORAL-SERGEANT

The Corporal was the first surface-to-surface missile to give the Army a nuclear capability.

It was first called the Corporal E and was a research rocket used in a joint program of the Army Ordnance and the Jet Propulsion Laboratory of the California Institute of Technology. It was taken from this category and developed into a modern artillery weapon, manufactured by the Firestone Tire and Rubber Company and Gilfillan Brothers. The original version of the Corporal had a range of about 50 miles, which was later increased to 100 miles.

The Corporal is 46 feet long and 2½ feet in diameter. It is command-guided and propelled by one liquid-propellant rocket engine.

This missile is a continuation of the German V-2 rocket system but with an improvement in the guidance system. Like the V-2, the Corporal follows a pre-set trajectory but its flight path can be corrected by signals from the ground, using computed data on the missile's flight, compared with the course planned for it.

Radio command control from the ground also shuts off the power plant when the correct missile velocity has been reached, feeds in a range correction velocity signal and arms the warhead at the time of range correction.

The Corporal is transported on a prime mover which acts as a crane to place the missile in launching position.

In spite of the Corporal's improved guidance system over that of the German V-2, its successor, the Sergeant, has an inertial guidance system.

The Sergeant is also propelled by a solid-propellant rocket engine and will have approximately twice the range of the Corporal or about 200 miles. It can be moved and stored more easily than the Corporal and its guidance system is highly invulnerable to enemy electronics countermeasures.

The Sergeant is a complete departure from the V-2 missile concept, incorporating much later technological developments, and represents a totally new weapon system as compared to the Corporal.

THE REDSTONE-PERSHING

The Army's Redstone surface-to-surface missile went into production by the Chrysler Corporation in 1956, after 10 years of development by the ex-German scientists of the Peenemunde group, working under the technical direction of the Army Ordnance engineers, first at Fort Bliss and later at the Army Missile Development Center, Redstone Arsenal, Huntsville, Alabama.

The Redstone, first static test fired in May of 1953, at the time of going into production had approximately the same range as the V-2 German missile, about 200 miles. However, the concept of the missile differed from that of the V-2, as well as from the original plan of the German scientists. The developmental Redstone program was intended to lead to a two-stage missile with a range of 1,500 miles.

The Redstone is 69 feet long and 5 feet in diameter. It is powered by a North American Aviation liquid-propellant rocket engine, with a thrust of 75,000 pounds. With a nuclear capability, the warhead is designed to separate from the missile vehicle.

The Redstone missile was used as the first stage of the Explorer I satellite-launching vehicle, the Jupiter-C. The Redstone was modified to burn hydrazine-based compound, instead of alcohol. This increased the thrust by about 12 per cent over the conventional Redstone engine. The first stage of the Jupiter-C burned for about 160 seconds and gave the Explorer a speed of approximately 6,800 miles per hour and an altitude of 53 miles.

The Department of Defense awarded new contracts to the Chrysler Corporation amounting to 21.8 million dollars for the continued production of the Redstone missile during the 1958 fiscal year.

The Redstone will be replaced by the Pershing, which is a solid-propellant version of the Redstone, having the same nuclear capability, but with much greater range.

It is planned for the Pershing to have a maximum range of about 800 miles, which is in the long-range missile category. It will thus keep the Army in the long-range missile field, even though the Air Force has been given operational control of the Army-developed Jupiter 1,500 mile IRBM.

Left: The Redstone
Right: The Sergeant

THE JUPITER

The Jupiter is one of the heavyweights in the surface-to-surface missile category, a 1,500-mile range IRBM, or Intermediate Range Ballistic Missile.

The Jupiter is 58 feet long and almost 9 feet in diameter. Its gross take-off weight is about 105,000 pounds, yet it has a maximum speed of Mach 12.

One liquid-propellant rocket engine, with about 150,000 pounds' thrust, propels the Jupiter and it is kept on its course by an inertial guidance system.

The Army Ballistic Missile Agency is responsible for the development of this weapon system. The Chrysler Corporation is the prime contractor, building missile shell and doing the assembly and systems-testing work. Goodyear Aircraft makes the nose cone and the Rocketdyne Division of North American Aircraft builds the rocket engine. This engine, by the way, is also used in the Air Force Thor IRBM. The inertial guidance system is built by the Ford Instrument Division of Sperry Rand Corporation.

The Jupiter is very closely related to the Redstone missile and much of the experience gained in experimentation with the Redstone has resulted in improved and modified components for the longer range Jupiter. Many of the parts of the two missiles are actually interchangeable.

Operational use of the Jupiter is the responsibility of the Air Force. A Jupiter squadron has fifteen of the missiles. In operation, a squadron will have six missiles positioned vertically on launchers and requiring only fifteen minutes of fueling and other preparations before firing. The entire six missiles can be fired at once. Six other missiles are kept nearby, ready to be erected and fired as soon as the first six have been fired. The other three missiles are kept in reserve and are not immediately ready for firing. From 600 to 650 persons are required in a Jupiter squadron.

The rocket engine operates on liquid oxygen and RP-1, which is a light cut kerosene. The propellants are delivered in trucks and are pumped into the missile just prior to the launching. Topping off of the propellant tanks is scheduled to be completed at two minutes before firing.

U. S. NAVY MISSILES

THE REGULUS I

Since 1955, the 500-mile range Regulus I surface-to-surface missile has been on duty aboard submarines, aircraft carriers, cruisers and other surface vessels of the Fleet, as well as land bases.

Built by Chance-Vought Aircraft, the Regulus I was the Navy's first operational attack missile, giving the sea service the ability to deliver a missile almost anywhere in the world. Rising silently from the depths of the ocean off an enemy coast, submarines could launch their missiles and submerge again before the deadly weapons struck their targets hundreds of miles inland. The Navy feels that the submarine provides a mobile, maneuverable launching base, virtually undetectable and, with atomic power, capable of operating continuously in all the oceans of the world.

The Regulus I is 33 feet long and has a wing span of 21 feet. Its Allison J33-A-18 turbojet engine gives it a speed very close to Mach 1 and a range of at least the rated 500 miles. An Aerojet-General solid-propellant rocket booster is used for launching.

The command guidance system is built by Sperry.

During the developmental period, the Regulus I was equipped with a landing gear and brake parachute, so that it could be recovered at a land base after test firing. It could be controlled back to the runway and landed by remote control.

The first successful Regulus I flight was made in 1951 but it did not become operational with the Fleet until four years later. By this time, a system of steam catapulting missiles from the decks of aircraft carriers had been developed. A special launching cart was produced by Chance Vought to make this kind of deck launching possible.

Chance Vought conceived the missile in 1947 and began its development under the sponsorship of the Navy Bureau of Aeronautics and four years later successfully flew the first Regulus I.

Navy Regulus I starting to take off on the stern of a cruiser

THE REGULUS II

The 1,000-mile plus range Regulus II guided surface-to-surface missile operates in the vicinity of Mach 2 speeds at altitudes of more than 50,000 feet and is operational from Navy submarines and surface ships.

Regulus II is 57 feet long and has a wing span of about 20 feet. It has a General Electric J79-GE-3 turbojet engine, with a rated thrust of more than 10,000 pounds. The AC Spark Plug Company produces the guidance system which is both command and inertial. Chance Vought Aircraft builds the missile itself.

The long-range Regulus II, like the 500-mile-range Regulus I, is designed for launching from submarines, aircraft carriers and cruisers and from shore bases. Similarly, training versions are equipped with landing gear so that missiles may be recovered after each flight.

In May, 1956, Regulus II made its first flight at Edwards Air Force Base, California. In response to the radio commands of a pilot in an accompanying chase plane, the huge missile rocketed across the dry lake bed for take-off, took steadily to the air, retracted its landing gear and climbed to 10,000 feet. Flying as smoothly as if a skilled pilot were aboard, the missile made a 90-degree turn at the prescribed point, settled into straight and level flight and made another 90-degree turn back toward the landing runway. More than 30 minutes after take-off, it touched down lightly on the lake bed and settled firmly to the ground, releasing its parachute to brake its speed.

Chance Vought's 1,000-miles-per-hour-plus F8U-1 Crusader was used as the chase plane for the Regulus II during the desert tests.

Except for size and performance, the Regulus I and the Regulus II are identical. Combined with the nuclear-powered submarine, the long-range Regulus II approached the ultimate naval weapon. Until the advent of more reliable means of underwater detection, the submarine-launched Regulus II will remain a potent weapon in the American arsenal.

A solid-propellant rocket built by Aerojet-General also serves as booster for the Regulus II.

Regulus I and Regulus II both can use a nuclear warhead.

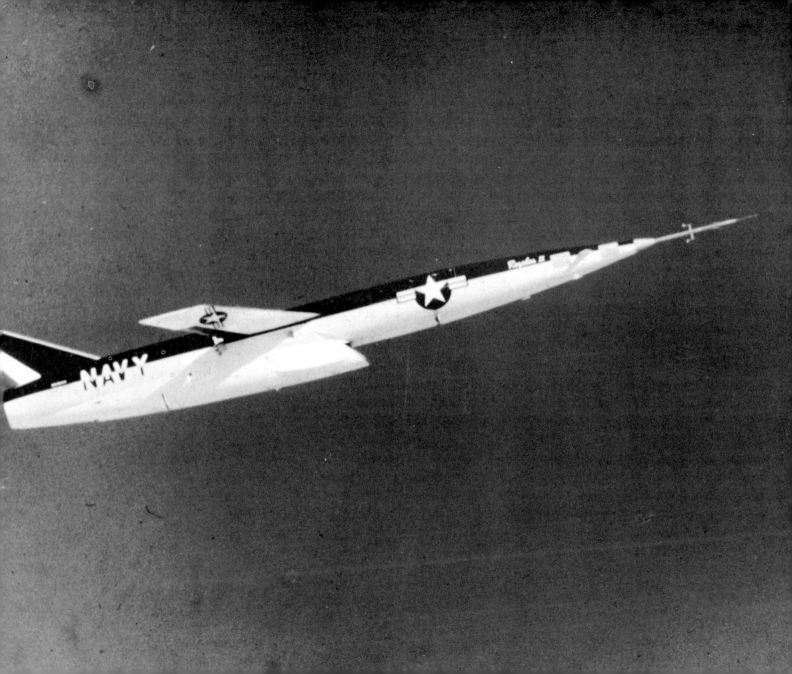

THE POLARIS

The Navy's foremost deterrent weapon is the submarine-launched Polaris, a solid-propellant intermediate range ballistic missile capable of delivering a nuclear warhead a distance of at least 1,500 miles.

The Polaris is unique in that it can be launched from beneath the surface of the sea, shot upward by compressed air. The rocket engine is timed to ignite a fraction of a second after the Polaris clears the water, at a height of 50 to 100 feet, and the missile begins its trip to the target.

Teamed with nuclear-powered submarines, the Navy feels the Polaris offers the maximum deterrent force because of the submarine's relative immunity to detection, plus the ability to launch the missile without surfacing. Nuclear power allows the submarine practically unlimited range and time at sea.

The Polaris is reported to be about 28 feet long and, if the configuration is similar to that of other missiles, this would indicate a diameter of approximately 3 feet.

The missile is manufactured by Lockheed Aircraft and the much-improved, solid-propellant rocket engine is produced by Aerojet-General Corporation. Earlier work on solid-propellants by both the Army and Air Force contributed much new information which was of importance in developing the Polaris powerplant.

Nine nuclear submarines make up the first complement of underseas ships designed to carry the Polaris. Each submarine can accommodate 16 of the missiles and the weapon system includes safeguards after enemy countermeasures.

Modification and development continues on the Polaris, the main objectives being to produce a lighter case and a lighter warhead, to give the missile great range with the present solid-propellant power plant.

The Polaris has an inertial guidance system. The submarines are navigated by the Ship's Inertial Navigation System, (SINS), developed by Dr. Stark Draper of M.I.T.

The Polaris is a worthy companion to the Thor and Jupiter in the IRBM class and another further power for peace.

ANTI-SUBMARINE MISSILES

While the anti-submarine missile usually is not included in the surface-to-surface missile category, this may be an appropriate place to consider it.

The principle of the missile does not adapt well to the concept of defense against submarines. The ballistic missile is basically a weapon of comparatively long range. The limitations imposed by the lack of any effective long-range detection system for underwater ships makes the missile incompatible as a part of a submarine defense plan.

However, the Navy has developed an anti-submarine weapon called the RAT which may not be a missile at all, but just what its name implies, a Rocket Assisted Torpedo. A casing and a rocket engine carry a torpedo from the launcher to a point over the target, where the casing separates, releasing the torpedo and allowing it to be dropped gently into the water by a small parachute. From then on the RAT becomes a torpedo, using an acoustical guidance system to find its target.

The RAT is 16 feet long and has a solid-propellant rocket booster.

The Petrel was a 24-foot missile with a 13-foot wing span and a 2-foot diameter which was propelled by a Fairchilds Engine Division J-44 turbojet engine and had a maximum speed of about Mach 0.7. This radar-homing missile has now been discontinued.

Several other anti-submarine missiles have been proposed by various manufacturers and have at least reached the research stage. Among these are the Astor, the Asroc and the Subroc.

However, the complete lack of success in adapting the missile to defense against submarines tends to corroborate the Navy's contention that the submarine, because of the extreme difficulty in detecting it, is the ideal launching platform for the Polaris IRBM.

U. S. AIR FORCE MISSILES

THE MATADOR-THE MACE

In 1946, the military gave specifications to the Martin Company for a surface-to-surface, medium range missile. Shortly after 4:30 p.m., on January 20, 1949, came the first official launching of an Air Force pilotless bomber, the Martin B-61 Matador.

The 6555th Guided Missile Wing, a unit of the Tactical Air Command, departed for Germany early in March of 1954, equipped with the Martin TM-61, to become the first unit of its type to be deployed overseas. Several others have followed it.

The USAF TM-61 Matador is about 40 feet long, 54 inches in diameter and has a wing span of almost 29 feet. Its operational altitude is over 35,000 feet. One Allison J33-A-37 turbojet engine gives it a speed of Mach 0.9, or about 650 miles per hour.

The Matador has been steadily improved since it became operational and the newest version of it has been given the name of The Mace.

The Martin TM-76 Mace — the "TM" in each case means "Tactical Missile" — is longer than the Matador, being 44 feet, with the same diameter of 54 inches. It has less wing span, measuring about 23 feet from tip-to-tip. It is propelled by the same Allison J33-A-37 turbojet engine, has a speed of over 650 miles per hour and is operational above 40,000 feet.

The Mace is launched from a highly mobile launcher, with the initial impetus furnished by a rocket booster. It has both high- and low-altitude capability and can use either a conventional or atomic warhead, the same as its predecessor, the Matador.

It can operate in any weather and is controlled by a ground crew and by inertial guidance.

Prior to the successful development of the Mace, the Navy's Regulus II was considered as a possible successor to the 500-mile range Matador. The Regulus II has a range of more than 1,000 miles and it is logical to expect the Mace to be modified and improved to increase its range beyond the initial 650 miles-plus.

The wings of the Mace are folded back against the body for transportation on the special launcher, which is towed by a multi-purpose truck, making previously inaccessible launching sites available.

THE SNARK

The Northrop SM-62 Snark is an Air Force Strategic Intercontinental Guided Missile, operational with the Strategic Air Command. The Snark has a range in excess of 5,000 miles and can carry a nuclear warhead.

This air-breathing missile is actually a pilotless aircraft, propelled by a single Pratt & Whitney J57 turbojet engine and guided by a combination stellar and inertial guidance system. Its speed is near Mach 1.

The Snark is launched by two high-thrust booster rockets, attached to the fuselage. As soon as the missile reaches its cruising speed, the booster rockets are jettisoned and the main turbojet engine takes over.

The Snark can be "zero" launched from a stationary or mobile launcher in a relatively small area. Both the missile and the launcher are extremely mobile and can be flown to any point in the world within a few hours. The missile and its ground support equipment are normally transported by C-124 Globemaster aircraft and can be set up in launch position within a short time after arrival at a given destination.

The Snark has an overall length of 69 feet, a wing span of 42 feet and stands 15 feet high. The tail consists only of a vertical stabilizer. Elevons, combination ailerons and elevators, on the trailing edge of the wings eliminate the need for a horizontal tail surface. Lack of a horizontal tail surface causes the Snark to have a relatively high angle of attack in flight.

Fuel is carried in the fuselage and in a pair of wing tanks streamlined into the wing structure. A system for the automatic transfer of fuel among the tanks maintains an acceptable center-of-gravity for the missile.

In operation, the Snark climbs rapidly to cruise altitude, then follows a straight line-of-flight to the target area at a speed of about Mach 0.9. Near its goal, it noses over into a terminal dive and hits the target at supersonic speed, bringing about its self-destruction upon impact.

The inertial guidance system, incorporating star-tracking, has proved to be extremely reliable. Northrop engineers developed this hybrid guidance system specifically for the Snark.

THE THOR

The Douglas Thor is the Air Force's Intermediate Range Ballistic Missile, capable of delivering a nuclear warhead a distance of at least 1,500 miles in a matter of minutes. It was developed as a part of a complete weapon system, with trained squadrons, fully equipped to support and operate the missile as soon as it became operational.

The Thor is 62 feet long, 8 feet in diameter and weighs about 110,000 pounds, yet it represents the maximum in strategic mobility. It can be packed up, transported, erected and operated almost anywhere.

The propulsion system is a Rocketdyne liquid-propellant rocket engine with a thrust of 165,000 pounds. An inertial guidance system controls the path of the Thor to the target.

Two vernier engines, placed 180 degrees apart, one on each side of the nozzle of the main rocket engine at the rear of the missile, give positive control of the Thor. The vernier engines are swiveled as needed, to twist or roll the missile into its intended trajectory. Using their own propellant, the verniers continue to function after the main engine has expended its fuel and cut out.

A Thor squadron is composed of between 500 and 600 persons and has 15 missiles. The squadron maintains complete strategic mobility. It is able to move the Thor from one area to another and still retain a reaction period that will permit the Thor to be fired in less time than it would take an enemy missile to fly from the adversary's target area.

All fifteen missiles in the squadron are kept ready for a fifteen-minute countdown and all can be fired simultaneously. The missiles lie in a horizontal position on their transporter-erectors, inside long, closed hangars. On an alert, the hangars are rolled away, the missile is hydraulically raised while still on the transporter-erector and placed in a vertical position. The transporter-erector is then moved away, leaving only a single servicing pole standing beside the missile as it rests on its base.

On firing, the Thor rises slowly from the pad, then accelerates quickly to over a dozen times the speed of sound as it carries devastating destruction to the enemy.

A Douglas Thor IRBM lifts from its launching pad at Cape Canaveral, Florida

THE ATLAS

The Atlas Intercontinental Ballistic Missile is our nearest approach to an ultimate weapon. A gigantic projectile which towers 75 feet into the air as it stands on its launching pad, about 10 feet in diameter, not including the two booster engines, capable of roaring toward an enemy target at twenty times the speed of sound, the Atlas carries the power to obliterate a whole city in one blow. It is difficult to comprehend the awesome force contained in the Atlas, a true intercontinental ballistic missile, with the capability of delivering a nuclear warhead at least 5,500 miles from the point of launching.

North American Aviation's Rocketdyne Division makes the liquid-propellant sustainer rocket engine which powers the Atlas. Two powerful rocket boosters, positioned on each side of the main, or sustainer engine, have a combined thrust of about 330,000 pounds, and are used in the launching and in the first few minutes of flight. The boosters and their associated equipment are then jettisoned, leaving the sustainer engine with a thrust of 60,000 pounds as the power source for the missile.

After the final engine shutoff, the nose cone separates from the missile and continues on alone to the target, carrying its nuclear load of annihilation.

The Atlas has an all-inertial guidance system developed by the American Bosch Arma Corporation. This system cannot be jammed or otherwise interfered with by enemy countermeasures and permits mass salvos of the missiles. It is dependent upon a series of gyro stabilizers very similar to the spinning toys familiar to most children. Such a guidance setup can operate well beyond the range of radio or radar guidance systems and is not dependent upon any type of ground control. It has its own computer and makes course corrections automatically.

Control of the Atlas in flight is accomplished by swiveling vernier engines, a technique developed by the Convair Division of the General Dynamics Corporation, the company chiefly responsible for the development of the Atlas. Convair worked stubbornly toward the present state of the art through the lean times of costly stop-and-go government spending and oscilating decisions, often spending company money to keep the Atlas project alive.

The Atlas rockets into the Florida sky

THE TITAN

The objective of the Titan ICBM Weapon System Program was to produce a ballistic missile which would use a different approach in performing the same basic mission as that of the Atlas, namely, delivering a thermonuclear warhead at a Mach 20 speed to an enemy target at least 5,500 miles away.

Development of the Titan has been a team effort of the Air Force, the Navy, the Martin Company, Univac Division of the Bell Telephone Company, the Avco Company and the Aerojet-General Corporation.

Physically, the Titan is quite similar to the Atlas. It is powered by three liquid-propellant rocket engines, developed by Aerojet-General. The production and test facilities were built from the ground up at Sacramento, California, especially to produce these engines for the Titan.

The Titan was designed to use either the American Bosch Arma Corporation all-inertial guidance system — the same as that of the Atlas — or a radio-command guidance system, developed by the Bell Telephone Laboratories and Remington Rand. The early models of the Titan were planned to use the radio-command system until the all-inertial system was produced in sufficient quantities to supply both the Atlas and the Titan.

Environmental testing of commercial equipment for the Titan was done by the Navy at the Naval Ordnance Test Station at Inyokern, California. The Martin Company built a special production facility at Denver, Colorado, to carry out the Titan program.

The Air Force has been asked why it is feasible to produce the Titan, which has basically the same mission and performance as the Atlas. The answer has been that it is better to use two different approaches to the solution of so important a problem, rather than to put all of our eggs into one basket. By working from two directions, we have an added element of assurance of success and the opportunity to discover and utilize more improvements in the whole ICBM program.

Although models of the Titan show a pointed nose, a blunt nose cone is used, which conforms with the configuration required for effective re-entry.

Model of Titan

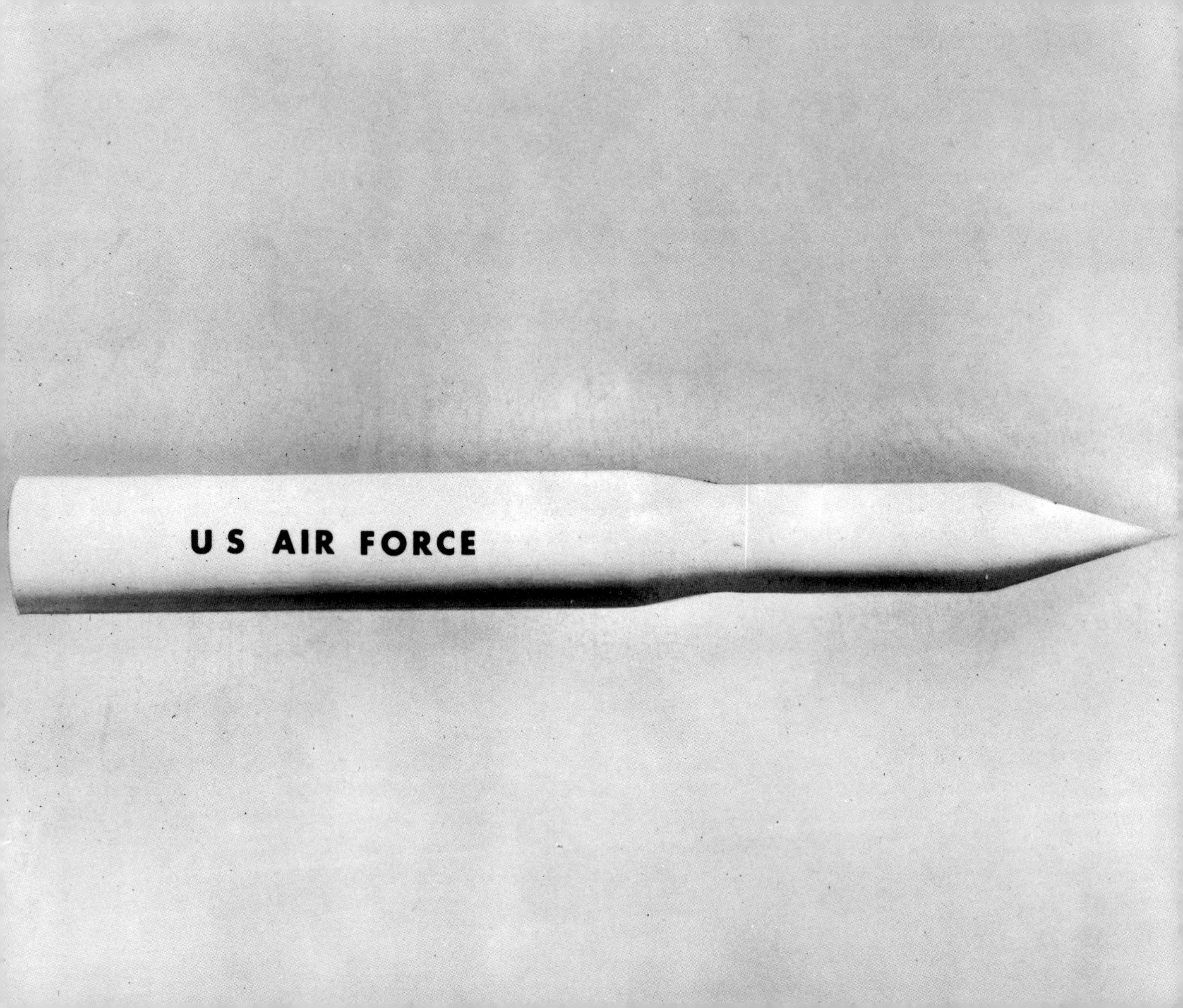
U S AIR FORCE

THE MINUTEMAN

The Minuteman is an Air-Force-developed, three-purpose, solid-propellant ballistic missile weapon system that can be employed as a tactical weapon or launched over intermediate and intercontinental ranges. With this variable capability, the Minuteman augments, and possibly could eventually replace, the Titan, Atlas and Thor.

Using only the third stage of the Minuteman, a range of from 500 to 1,000 miles is attained, making it ideal for use as a tactical weapon. A combination of the second and third stages gives the Minuteman an intermediate, or 1,500 mile range, and allows it to operate in the same area as the Thor and Jupiter. When all three stages are used, intercontinental ballistic missile range is possible.

The Minuteman is the first ballistic missile to be designed specifically for launching from underground sites. This is a move to diminish the vulnerability to enemy attack of fixed base missile launching facilities.

The Air Force and the Navy have worked closely together in developing the Minuteman and the Polaris. Earlier Air Force work on solid propellants was the basis for Navy advances in the propulsion system of the Polaris. The Navy is using the Air Force-developed propellant motor case and lightweight nozzle. This is still another example of the free interchange of information and knowledge among the services.

The Minuteman is able to employ an all-inertial guidance system. However, the Navy has a much greater problem in this area than the other services because of limited space in the launching submarine and the need for an underwater launch.

Several firms have played important roles in developing the multi-stage, solid-propellant engines for the Minuteman. Among them are the Thiokol Corporation, Aerojet-General and Phillips Petroleum. The general concept of the propellant is an outgrowth of the pioneering work done in developing Air Force JATO units to assist B-47 take-offs.

The Minuteman program has drawn heavily on the experience gained by all three services in developing ballistic missiles and the engines to propel them. It is a result of the free interchange of technical data among them.

GROUND-LAUNCHED RESEARCH VEHICLES

In the development of missiles, there have been so many research and test vehicles and rockets that space permits consideration of only a few of them. Those described here are the most recent ones and not necessarily the most important.

Lockheed's X-7 ramjet missile is a ground-controlled, pilotless aircraft, used to test ramjet engines. In performing this mission it has reached supersonic speeds and extremely high altitudes. The X-7 parachutes to earth after completing its mission and can be used over and over again. It is launched from a B-29 mother ship at a high altitude.

North American Aviation's X-10 is quite similar but is even more like an airplane in that it has a tricycle landing gear and a deceleration parachute to slow its landing roll out. It is powered by two Westinghouse J-40-1 turbojet engines and has successfully flown hundreds of miles at supersonic speed and under full automatic control. The mission of the X-10 was to obtain data at supersonic speed on aerodynamic design, control and automatic guidance systems. This data was helpful in developing the Navaho intercontinental strategic guided missile, which was later diverted to a research missile role itself.

Lockheed's X-17 research rocket is a test missile which was used to prove nose cone designs. A 40-foot tall projectile missile, the X-17's first stage is a single, large, solid-propellant rocket. The second stage is a cluster of three Recruit rockets, and the third stage is a single Recruit rocket, all built by the Thiokol Corporation. The first stage blasts the 6-ton bird off the launching pad at Cape Canaveral, Florida, to an altitude of several miles in a few seconds.

The X-17 then follows a looping trajectory, coasting upward to its peak altitude in the thin air of the ionosphere. Without sufficient air to provide aerodynamic control, it drops tail-first to an altitude where denser air begins to turn its nose downward. At this point, the first stage is ejected and the second stage, a cluster of three rockets, is ignited. The missile again roars into life, this time, on a headlong plunge down through the atmosphere.

In a matter of a few seconds, this second stage has belched out a tremendous surge of power and is discarded. Simultaneously with this ejection, the third and final stage, with the nose cone, fires and drives the X-17 downward at an even more fabulous speed, subjecting the nose shape being tested to the extremely high temperatures necessary to test the design.

The whole flight takes just a little more than six minutes, during which the X-17 continuously radios to ground stations vast quantities of information on velocity, acceleration, heat and other performance.

The HTV is an Air Force vehicle which gets its name from the fact that it is a "hypersonic test vehicle." Built by the Aerophysics Development Corporation, the HTV is 13 feet long, about 10 inches in diameter and is propelled by 11 solid-propellant rockets to a maximum speed of Mach 7.

The Wasp is a solid-propellant, weather-sounding vehicle in use by the Navy in meteorological studies of the upper atmosphere. No specific information is available on it.

The Hasp is another Navy weather rocket, propelled to an altitude of about 20 miles by a Grand Central solid-propellant rocket. The Hasp is 6 feet long and about 4 inches in diameter.

The Army, Navy and Air Force use the Aerobee sounding rocket, which can carry a 150-pound load of instrumentation to an altitude of 70 miles. It is 19 feet long and slightly over one foot in diameter and is propelled by an Aerojet liquid-propellant rocket.

The Aerobee II, used by the Navy and Air Force, is 21 feet long, also slightly more than one foot in diameter. Its Aerojet liquid-propellant engine permits it to take a 150-pound payload to an altitude of 170 miles.

The NACA (National Advisory Committee for Aeronautics) is planning to use the Deacon sounding rocket, which is about 9 feet long and 6 inches in diameter. It is powered by a solid-propellant rocket. The entire rocket is made by the Allegheny Ballistics Laboratories.

The Cajun, built by the University of Michigan for the Air Force, is over 13 feet long, has fins giving it a wing span of about 2 feet and has a 6-inch diameter. It is propelled by a Thiokol solid-propellant rocket to a maximum speed of Mach 6.5. This is also a sounding rocket.

Several other sounding rockets are either in use or in the developmental stage.

THE NAVAHO

One of the most secret of all missile developments was the North American XSM-64, a supersonic intercontinental guided missile known by the popular name of Navaho. With the cancellation of the project in July, 1957, some information was released and, with subsequent test firings of several of the missiles in stock, photographs were made available to the press.

The Navaho is powered by two Wright RJ-47 ramjet engines and is therefore in the air-breather category. On launching, the Navaho rides piggyback on a large Rocketdyne booster, which is said to develop a maximum thrust of 270,000 pounds, making it one of the most powerful boosters of its kind. There are two thrust chambers in the booster. At a pre-determined altitude and speed, the Navaho separates from the booster, which drops clear and burns itself out, then the two RJ-47 ramjet engines take over to propel the missile on its intercontinental journey.

The Navaho has an inertial and infrared homing guidance system. The delta wings of the missile have aerodynamically-balanced control surfaces at the tips.

Just as there is no such thing as an unsuccessful missile-firing, since each firing contributes to the general fund of knowledge, the Navaho Project has added much important information about ramjet engines and the vehicles they can propel. Cancellation certainly does not mean failure.

THE JUPITER C

The advent of Sputnik One set the stage for a test vehicle to gain world attention under the name of Jupiter C.

When the Russian satellite went into orbit, the Navy's Vanguard Project was moving steadily along on a schedule which would have launched a satellite during the international Geophysical Year, as planned. With the realization of the full impact of Sputnik One, the Navy was urged to rush the project and actual test vehicles were used in an attempt to launch a satellite. With the almost inevitable failures resulting, the Army Ballistic Missile Agency was given a chance to have a try at putting the United States back in contention. A Jupiter C was devised and Explorer One went into orbit.

Two closeups of North American's Navaho being set for launching

The Jupiter-C was a four-stage rocket, a modified Redstone being the first stage. The other fifteen solid-propellant rockets were scaled down Sergeants, designed and developed by the Jet Propulsion Laboratory of the California Institute of Technology in 1949.

Jupiter C gained considerable more sophistication by the time it was used to launch Explorer IV in its quest of new knowledge of the radiation field around the earth's atmosphere.

THE VANGUARD

The Vanguard is a three-stage carrier for the Naval Research Laboratory's satellites. Built by the Martin Company, the Vanguard is a highly sophisticated satellite vehicle, designed solely for the purpose of launching an instrumented sphere into orbit.

In October, 1956, an official of the Martin Company stated that the average would be considered good if one out of twelve Vanguard test launchings could result in a successful orbit of a satellite. Through five unsuccessful launchings, the Vanguard Project smarted under repeated accusations of failure, emphasized by the Jupiter-C launching of Explorer I, until finally, with test launching number six, at 3.25-pound sphere was placed into an orbit, with a 2,513 mile apogee, and the Vanguard Project began to get recognition as one of the most advanced and effective programs in the relatively short Missile Age.

The Vanguard is 72 feet long and slightly less than 4 feet in diameter. The first stage engine is a General Electric liquid-propellant engine; the second stage is an Aerojet-General liquid-propellant engine and the third stage is a Grand Central solid-propellant rocket engine.

Most of the energy required to get the satellite to orbital height and about 15 per cent of the required orbital velocity is supplied by the first stage. The second stage gets the third stage of the satellite to orbital height and attains 32 per cent of the orbital velocity. The third stage supplies the remaining force needed to place the satellite in orbit.

Each firing of the Vanguard has marked an improvement in some phase of the program. Many of the early failures were due to the extreme sophistication of the missile. An example of this is found in the fact that the Vanguard must be exactly vertical at time of launching. This requirement is so critical that precise optical tooling devices are used to check the missile for proper positioning before firing. It is evident that even windy conditions could easily have a disastrous effect upon a launching.

It should be emphasized that the Vanguard I satellite went farther into space than any of the other satellites which preceeded it, either Russian or American. Explorer III reached an apogee of 1,741 miles, Sputnik III, 1,720 miles. The 2,513 mile apogee established by Vanguard I thus reached much farther into the strange and unknown areas of space.

THE PIED PIPER

In the evolution of man-made satellites it is only natural that instrument-carrying spheres would be followed by a satellite which could send back visual evidence from its path in space. Such a satellite is the Pied Piper, an Air Force reconnaissance vehicle, developed by the Lockheed Aircraft Company.

The Pied Piper is designed to carry optical cameras, television cameras, radar or infrared scanning devices, whichever means of visual reporting seems most suitable for the particular mission of the satellite.

Weighing from 1 to 1½ tons, the Pied Piper can be launched by a modification of the Atlas missile as a booster. A solid propellant of special design is attached to the satellite and gives it the final thrust needed to enter its orbit.

Somewhat lighter reconnaissance satellites have been designed for the Army by RCA and would weigh a maximum of 700 pounds in the television camera versions.

LUNAR PROBES

As man-made earth satellites continue to progress in the study of the relatively immediate space in the vicinity of the earth, scientists are moving on farther into space to seek answers from lunar probes. Both the Army and the Air Force have projects with this objective.

The Air Force began working on the lunar probe program by scheduling a series of test firings known as Project Able and Project Able I, using the Thor intermediate range ballistic missile as a first stage and the Aerojet-General Vanguard second stage liquid-propellant rocket engine. In April, 1958, using this Project Able combination of a Douglas Thor and an Aerojet second stage, the Air Force sent a test missile over 4,000 miles into space to gather valuable data. Receiving most news attention was the live mouse carried in a scaled-down nose cone during this series of firings. However, the real purpose of the test was to get information leading to a lunar probe.

For the actual attempt to place a missile in the vicinity of the moon, a third stage engine was added and the test missile was called Thor-Able I. An Allegheny Ballistics Laboratory solid-propellant rocket engine was used for the third stage. For some of the moon shots, another stage called the "terminal stage" was planned. This is a rocket which could be fired on a command signal, to give the missile additional thrust as it began to parallel the moon's orbit.

Plans were made for the initial probes to merely reach the vicinity of the moon, with an impact upon the moon's surface being the least desirable of possible developments. It was hoped the probe would get to within at least 10,000 miles of the moon, either passing on by it, or, if correctly affected by the moon's gravitational field, going on around the moon and back to the earth's atmosphere. This would provide data on the hitherto dark side of the moon. Other possibilities were that the probe might go into orbit indefinitely around the moon or might even establish a figure-eight orbit around both the moon and the earth.

This Air Force project was named Operation Mona and the Army's project was called Juno II. A Jupiter first stage and various combinations of the Sergeant and scaled-down Sergeant were planned to be included in this project. The Naval Ordnance Test Station at Inyokern, California, developed the ground-scanning device used in the moon probe projects.

The follow-up of the lunar probes would be instrumented payloads, landed on the surface of the moon and capable of reporting back data to further Man's exploration of space.

Part 7 / MAN IN SPACE

There is actually no line of demarcation between the atmosphere and space. No person can definitely state where space begins.

One avenue to true space is through the evolution and development of manned aircraft. By flying faster and higher and longer, manned aircraft get nearer and nearer to becoming manned spacecraft. Following this approach, the men of the Air Force have become accustomed to a region in the fringe of space which is unknown and unfamiliar to all other men.

It began with the seeking of a solution to the strange behavior of World War Two military aircraft as they accelerated close to the speed of sound. The Bell X-1 rocket-powered, manned aircraft was built to penetrate the barrier which kept airplanes from going faster. Lieutenant Colonel Chuck Yeager pushed the X-1A on through the sonic barrier to a Mach 2.5 speed to become the first USAF pilot to fly faster than sound. Lieutenant Colonel Pete Everest flew the X-2, successor to the X-1, at 1,900 miles per hour on July 26, 1956. Captain Iven Kincheloe topped this speed and on September 7, 1956 climbed the X-2 to the incredible altitude of 126,000 feet, nearer to space than any other person had ever been. Major David Simons reached 102,000 feet in a balloon and provided additional proof that Man can adapt to space. On September 27, 1956, Captain Milburn Apt attained a speed of 2,178 miles per hour in the X-2 and lost his life in an unexplained crash moments later.

The flights of the X-1 and X-2 paved the way for the development of our present crop of supersonic aircraft and evolved into the X-15 program, which was designed to take Man into an area where conventional aerodynamic controls no longer function because of the thinness of the air — or the lack of it — and permit him to learn the use of astronautical controls in guiding the aircraft which had suddenly become a spacecraft. Moving into space by this method, Man could also learn how to get back from space, controlling his vehicle in a pattern of decelerating gliding which slows his craft sufficiently to allow re-entry into the atmosphere without burning up from passing through the heavier air too fast.

Just as the Bell X-1 and X-2 experimental aircraft made possible the supersonic aircraft now operational in the Air Force, so the North American Aviation X-15 will supply the information and techniques which will produce the hypersonic vehicles capable of circumnavigating the earth many times before re-entering the atmosphere. Alternative methods of launching such vehicles are already known and proven. They may be launched from the surface, using IRBM and ICBM missiles as boosters, or they may be launched from a mother ship at high altitudes as in the case of the X-1, X-2 and X-15. The latter method allows the tremendous acceleration required to be started at the discretion of the pilot.

The X-15 program represents a cautious, step-by-step advance into space, a walk-before-you-run procedure. The first step in this realistic pattern is perfection of the launching techniques from the modified B-52 mother ship and a complete demonstration of the gliding characteristics of the X-15 in its controlled flight back to a landing.

The X-15 test range stretches from Wendover Air Force Base, Utah, to Edwards Air Force Base, California, a distance which accommodates the estimated 450-mile range of the X-15.

The X-15 is carried aloft under the right wing of a B-52 and released at approximately 40,000 feet. The experimental craft then flies a carefully calculated test program, terminating in a dead stick landing at Edwards. Data-gathering instrumentation is located at Edwards and Wendover, with intermediate stations at Beatty and Ely, Nevada. Culmination of the series of test flights is expected to produce a speed of about 3,600 miles per hour and reach an altitude of from 100 to 300 miles.

After the flights into Space by the X-15, the project to follow in logical sequence is called the Dyna-Soar Program. This program is intended to produce an orbital bomber which incorporates the characteristics of a hypersonic boost-glide vehicle, to give it greater flexibility and mission capability in its military application. Any vehicle following a fixed orbital path, such as the man-made earth satellites, would be extremely vulnerable to enemy counteraction. For this reason, the Dyna-Soar Program must develop a method of control which will allow the orbital bomber to alter its path and to be returned to the atmosphere at the will of the pilot.

While in orbit, the Dyna-Soar vehicle could continuously perform a reconnaissance mission, and upon departing from orbit, would immediately become a hypersonic weapon system, capable of controlled evasive action and having the range capability to place a megaton bomb on any target on earth.

The alternative method of putting a man in space, by means of a surface launched vehicle, is being

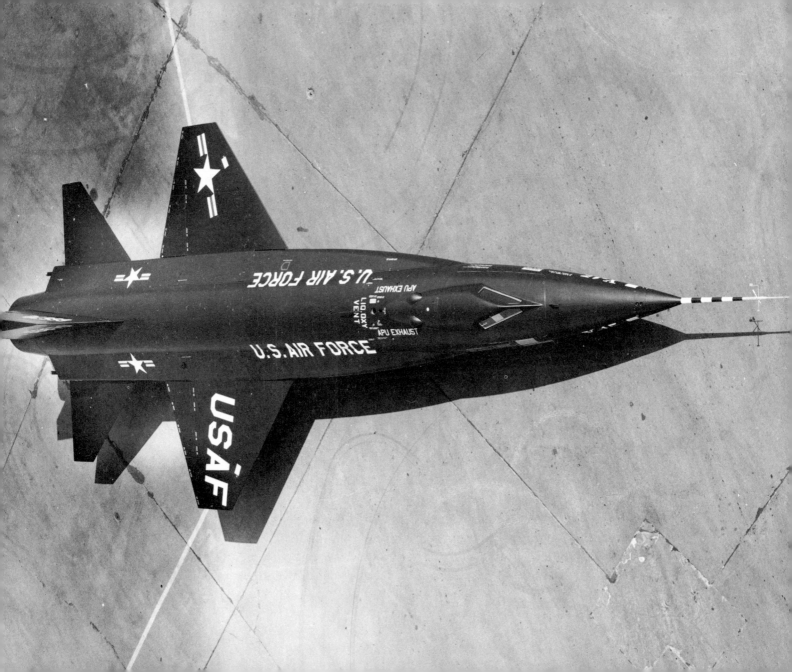

developed concurrently with the X-15-Dyna-Soar approach. After Man is projected into space in a capsule for a space flight which proves primarily that he can exist under such conditions and during the process can exercise powers of judgment, the next step will be to give him complete control of the vehicle in which he rides, with the ability to return eventually from his space trip to a safe landing on earth or on the oceans.

With the knowledge gained from lunar probe projects, from subsequent moon-impact rockets which will deliver instruments to the moon's surface to report back vital information and with the further development of power sources which use the elements of space to provide propulsion, Man may be able to begin his exploration of the universe by a trip to the moon.

Krafft A. Ehricke of the Convair Astronautics Division of the General Dynamics Corporation, envisions a vehicle, launched by a missile similar to the Atlas ICBM, using nuclear power to move through space and employing retro-rockets to permit it to slowly back down onto the surface of the moon, with the retro-rockets acting to counterbalance the pull of the moon's gravitational field. The vehicle would carry sufficient fuel to return to a position just outside the earth's atmosphere, at which point the crew would transfer to a re-entry glider for the return to earth.

No matter how he gets there, complete utilization of space awaits Man's entry into it. Rockets, missiles, lunar probes are but extensions of Man's inquisitive mind, reaching for the knowledge that will permit him to project himself into this new environment. When he is able to do this freely and usefully, we will have moved on into the Space Age.

We cannot hope to gain control of space, either militarily or commercially, but we must have the capability to keep any other nation from doing so. We must keep pace with all nations as we advance into the utilization of space.

If we do not plan for the future, we can hope for no future. Our survival, physically and economically, depends upon our ability to compete in this new dimension.

As our satellites and missiles probe farther and farther in Man's quest for knowledge, we will gradually diminish the need for the conventional manned aircraft of the Strategic Air Command, which have

Conception of moon landing

given us the deterrent power to preserve peace in the world. We cannot simply jettison this power into obsolescence but must carefully expand it into its eventual space application. Our judgment must be precisely correct in selecting the types and quantities of the weapon systems available to us as we pass through this fantastically dangerous transition from the Air Age to the Space Age. Our greatest danger may lie in Man's inclination to misinterpret the true meaning of the Missile Age and his eagerness to accept the ballistic missile as the culmination of the military art.

We Americans are in a grave hour of our life as a free nation. We desperately need to understand the significance of the relationships among the Air Age, the Missile Age and the Space Age. Right now, we stand in knowledge of the Space Age at the same point, perhaps, where the Wright Brothers stood in knowledge of the Air Age at Kitty Hawk in 1903. Aggressive world Communism will not permit us another leisurely fifty-five years to complete the conquest of space. Space and velocity are interdependent and we must speed up our search for knowledge, advancing as rapidly as possible beyond each new frontier.

We face a situation calling for an expediency far different from that which clustered together a bunch of rockets to launch our first tiny satellite. Our need is for a dedication of ourselves and our resources to an intelligent program for progress in space, a program with the vision to anticipate and plan for our essential requirements for existence.

We need a public which is so well informed on the issues of the day that it will demand and get the positive leadership we must have if we are to endure and benefit from the Space Age.

We have the ability, we must find the will.

GLOSSARY

ANTI-MISSILE MISSILE — A defensive missile and the system which supports it by detecting, identifying, tracking and the guidance of the defensive missile to an impact with the attacking missile.

ASTRAGATION — Space navigation.

APOGEE — The point in an orbital path which is farthest from the earth.

ASTRONAUTICS — The science of space travel, including propulsion systems and space vehicles.

ATMOSPHERIC BRAKING — Maneuvering of a manned satellite or space vehicle to use atmospheric drag to decelerate to a speed slow enough to allow passage through the thermal thicket.

BALLISTIC MISSILE — A missile which follows a ballistic trajectory to its target.

BALLISTIC TRAJECTORY — Portion of the path of a ballistic missile where no propulsion or steering is used. Also called free flight.

BEAM-RIDER — A missile which is guided by a system designed to follow a radar beam from either the ground or an airplane to the target.

BOOST-GLIDE BOMBER — A vehicle which is propelled upward by rocket engines, either from ground-launch or air-launch, and then uses a method of skipping along the atmosphere as a stone skips on water to go long distances. Aerodynamic surfaces allow it to do this and to make a controlled landing after atmospheric braking.

COMMAND RADAR — A guidance system for a missile which is controlled by ground radio signals and tracked by radar.

COSMIC RAYS — These are particles from interstellar space which are constantly entering the atmosphere at extremely high speed. Extensive exposure to cosmic rays is potentially harmful to humans.

ESCAPE VELOCITY — The speed at which an object is able to leave the gravitational field of a planet without further propulsion. The speed required to leave the earth's atmosphere and field of gravity is a little more than 25,000 miles per hour or 7 miles per second.

GUIDANCE SYSTEM — The method by which the track of a missile to its target is determined and how the missile is kept on its course.

HOMING-ACTIVE — A guidance system which tracks its target by emitting some type of waves of energy, such as infrared or radar.

HOMING-PASSIVE — A guidance system which tracks down moving aircraft or missiles through sound, light, heat or radio waves emitted by the target.

HYPERSONIC — A speed five or more times the speed of sound.

INERTIAL — A guidance device which steers the missile and is self-contained with the missile and is not dependent upon any outside control.

LUNAR PROBE — An unmanned missile propelled into space with the correct course and speed to circumnavigate or land on the moon. Purpose is the collection of information and data.

MACH NUMBER — Speed of an object relative to the speed of sound. Mach 2, for example, means twice the speed of sound.

ORBIT — Path made by a satellite in moving around the body to which it belongs. The moon is a natural satellite of the earth.

ORBITAL BOMBER — Another name for a Boost-Glide Bomber.

ORBITAL VELOCITY — The speed required to put a body in orbit. In the case of the earth, orbital velocity is 18,000 miles per hour.

PAD — A constructed surface from which missiles are launched.

PERIGEE — The point in an orbital path which is nearest to the earth, or other parent body.

PAYLOAD — That portion of a missile's total weight which consists of useful cargo, either instrumentation or warheads.

RE-ENTRY — Entry back into the earth's atmosphere of a missile, warhead or satellite after a trip into space.

STELLAR GUIDANCE — A guidance system which steers a missile by taking reference information from the stars. Also called Celestial Guidance.

SUBSONIC — A speed less than the speed of sound.

SUPERSONIC — A speed up through four times the speed of sound.

TELEMETERING — Instrumentation to measure the reactions of materials and matter. In missile use, this information is radioed back to earth on a reserved portion of the radio broadcast spectrum.

VERNIER — A small rocket engine or nozzle, mounted on a missile in such a manner as to be able to control the missile's direction. Also used to establish precise final velocity for orbit or escape.

WARHEAD — The destructive portion of a missile, intended to cause damage to an enemy, and the casing which incloses it.

WEIGHTLESSNESS — The point in the atmosphere at which centrifugal force exactly equals the pull of gravity, resulting in a total lack of weight. In space, this condition is ever-present unless some artificial means of creating gravity is employed within a space vehicle.

INDEX

Aerobee 80
Air Force Missiles 68
Air-To-Air Missiles 17
Air-To-Surface Missiles 27
Ajax 36
Anti-Submarine Missiles 67
Apt, Captain Milburn 87
Army Missiles 54
Asp 26
Asroc 67
Astor 67
Atlas 74

Ballistic Missile Early
    Warning System 42
Bomarc 50
Bulldog 30
Bull Goose 52
Bullpup 30

Cajun 80
Cherokee 26

Congreve, Sir William 7
Corporal 56
Corvus 32
Crossbow 32

Dart 54
Deacon 80
Diamondback 22
Dornberger, Dr. Walter R. 7
Dyna-Soar Project 88

Electromagnetic Energy 48
Everest, Lt. Col. "Pete" 87
Explorer 82

F-104 15
Falcon 18
Farside Project 26
Fury 31
Future Air-To-Surface
    Missiles 33

GAR 18
Genie 20
Gimlet 32
Goddard, Robert H. 7
Green Quail 33

Hasp 80
Hawk 36
Hercules 36
Honest John 54
Hound Dog 28
HTV 80

Juno II 86
Jupiter 60
Jupiter C 82

Kincheloe, Captain Iven 87

Lacrosse 54
Little John 54
Lunar Probes 85

Mace 68
Man In Space 87
Matador 68
Minuteman 78
Missile Age, The 13
Missile Defense Systems 42
Moon landing 90

Navaho 82
Navy Missiles 62
Nike 36
Nike-Ajax 36
Nike-Hercules 36
Nike-Zeus 36
Nike-Zeus System 44

Oberth, Hermann 7

Pershing 58
Petrel 67
Pied Piper 85
Plato System 45
Polaris 66

Project Able 86

Rascal 28
RAT 67
Redstone 58
Regulus I 62
Regulus II 14, 64
Research Missiles 26, 79
Rockaire 26

Schenk, Peter J. 7
Sergeant 56
Sidewinder 22
Simons, Maj. David 87
Skokie 26
Snark 70
Sparrow 24
Sputnik 7
Subroc 67
Surface-to-Air Missiles 35
Surface-to-Surface Missiles 53

Talos 38

Tartar 38
Terrier 40
Thor 72
Titan 76

Vanguard Project 84
Von Braun, Wernher 8

Wagtail 32
Wasp 80
Wizard System 45

X-1 87
X-2 87
X-7 79
X-10 79
X-15 88
X-17 79

Yeager, Lt. Col. Charles 87

Zeus 36
Zuni 24